D1279040

NATIONAL GEOGRAPHIC

NOVEMBER 2009 · VOL. 216 · NO. 5

CHARLIE HAMILTON JAMES

This kingfisher will smack the minnow in its beak against a branch, then swallow it. The minnow at right leaped to safety. Story on page 76.

NATIONAL GEOGRAPHIC

DEPARTMENTS

ngm.com

Last Call for Photos October 31 is the last day for English-language edition readers to enter the International Photo Contest. Winners earn prizes and a spot in the final competition.

GREG VORE

On the Cover

Two thousand years ago this Egyptian cat was killed and mummified. A pilgrim probably bought it to offer to a god, along with a prayer.

Photo by Richard Barnes

FOR SUBSCRIPTIONS, GIFT MEMBERSHIPS, OR CHANGES OF ADDRESS, CONTACT CUSTOMER SERVICE AT *NGMSERVICE.COM*, OR CALL 1-800-NGS-LINE (647-5463). OUTSIDE THE U.S. AND CANADA PLEASE CALL +1-813-979-6845.

EDITOR'S NOTE

Photographer Stephen Alvarez shoots from a stone spire in Tsingy de Bemaraha national park and reserve.

It happened to Stephen Alvarez, as it does to many photographers. He looked at a few pictures from an exotic landscape, in this case Madagascar, and thought, How hard can it be to photograph that place?

As you'll see from the photographs he made for this month's story "Living on a Razor's Edge," it is hard. Really hard. To begin, it took him five days to trek to Tsingy de Bemaraha national park and reserve from Madagascar's capital, Antananarivo. When he, writer Neil Shea, and a team of scientists reached the area's rugged limestone towers, they had to pick their way along knife-edge ridges that dropped off into 400-foot-deep canyons. "It was like walking on a pile of steak knives," Stephen says. "I had little fear of falling 400 feet. The real fear was falling six inches and slicing my femoral artery."

Because the going was so arduous, the team felt lucky to cover half a mile in a single day. One afternoon Neil tripped over a vine and landed on a sharp spike of limestone that punctured his knee nearly to the bone. It took two painful days for him to reach a nurse who treated the wound. She asked why he would ever want to go to a place like the *tsingy.* The answer is easy. Really easy. It's because the tsingy is the kind of exotic, unexplored place *National Geographic* magazine has taken readers to for more than a century.

Chris Johns

PHOTO: LUKE PADGET

Greater Bamboo Lemur
(Prolemur simus)
Size: Head and body length, 40 - 42 cm (15.7 - 16.5 inches); tail, 45 - 58 cm (17.7 - 22.8 inches)
Weight: 2.2 - 2.5 kg (4.9 - 5.5 lbs)
Habitat: Forest patches with bamboo in the south-central portion of the eastern rainforest of Madagascar
Surviving number: Estimated at fewer than 160

Photographed by Iñaki Relanzón

WILDLIFE AS CANON SEES IT

On the menu: bamboo, bamboo and more bamboo. The greater bamboo lemur is one of the few creatures on Earth to depend on a diet of bamboo. It lives in small groups, generally of four to seven, and is active at dawn, dusk and into the night. Populations are highly fragmented, sometimes hundreds of miles apart, as the lemur is found only in those patches of forest where its mainstay meal still grows. These bamboo oases are besieged by deforestation due to agriculture and logging. What's more, the lemur is regularly hunted for food. Once widespread, this bamboo connoisseur is now one of the world's most endangered primates.

As we see it, we can help make the world a better place. Raising awareness of endangered species is just one of the ways we at Canon are taking action—for the good of the planet we call home. Visit **canon.com/environment** to learn more.

NATIONAL GEOGRAPHIC

Inspiring people to care about the planet

The National Geographic Society is chartered in Washington, D.C., as a nonprofit scientific and educational organization "for the increase and diffusion of geographic knowledge." Since 1888 the Society has supported more than 9,000 explorations and research projects, adding to knowledge of earth, sea, and sky.

Contributions to the National Geographic Society are tax deductible under Section 501(c)(3) of the U.S. tax code.

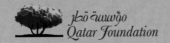

LETTERS

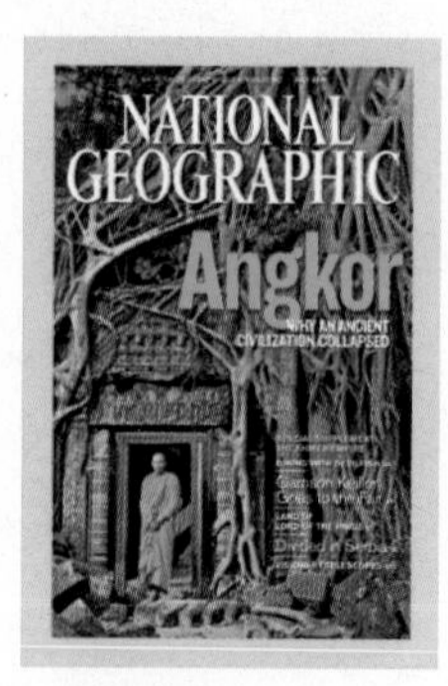

July 2009

Top Ten State Fair Joys

I enjoyed Garrison Keillor's honest and lively description, but in my 79 years, I have gone only once to a state fair. I found it so noisy, bizarre, weird, and gross that I made it a point never to go again, which explains why I am still sane.

BOB SAXTON
Eugene, Oregon

Being Finnish, I've always found the fascination for "twisted" or "evil" fairs present in the horror-fiction genre to be somewhat baffling, but this piece gave great insight into the phenomenon. It was an interesting glimpse into American culture.

ANTTI VJ NIEMELÄ
Helsinki, Finland

Reading this article, I sadly realized that Garrison Keillor, once a barometric proponent of all that was and is good about Americana, has been reduced to a bitter pessimist. Having myself attended fine state fairs in Iowa, Illinois, Wisconsin, and California, I only hope that Keillor may yet live through his own cathartic *Christmas Carol* night, during which he is visited by the ghosts of state fairs past, present, and future. He might emerge a new man, coming back to his listeners and readers as the wry and insightful commentator we have long admired—corn dog and cheesecake on a stick in hand.

DEAN G. LOUMBAS
San Francisco, California

Midwesterners are "abstemious"? Maybe I am foggy on the meaning of that word, but judging from the picture on pages 70-71, it looks to me as if Iowans are eating state fair fare 365 days a year.

KAY TESKE
Virginia Beach, Virginia

What a brilliantly articulated story. I easily slipped into the Midwest summer and lost myself among the corn-dog-chomping crowds. State—or in our case, county—fairs are a wonderful respite from the maddeningly boring and sterile workdays we endure in our "real" lives.

HILARY AMOLINS
Consecon, Ontario

My husband and I met at the San Mateo County Fair in 1946. What fond memories we still have. Every part of that magical place still holds us after 61 years of marriage. No one we talk to understands, since present-day state fairs are not at all the same. In 1946, fairs were a social occasion. The carnival portion was a small part. The exhibits and entertainment were unforgettable.

MINA PRATT
Oakhurst, California

Your article reminded me of an experience I had at the Washington County Fair in New York a few years ago. I happened upon a girl—she could not have been more than eight—washing her sheep in preparation for a later showing. She didn't see me. When the animal was well sudsed up, she paused, went to the sheep's head, and said softly, "Even if we don't win, I want you to know that you are the most beautiful sheep here." It seems to me that when you get through the rides, the foods, and the carnival atmosphere, what stands out about state fairs is the purity of values in our young people's fair exhibits. Incidentally, her sheep came in second, but it really didn't matter. The animal already knew how beautiful it was.

IRV WEST
Thurman, New York

The Serbs: One Nation Divisible

Even the subtitle of this story seems to mock the sad fate of the Serbs—carved up between several countries, disinherited, and disenfranchised.

NEBOJSA MALIC
Arlington, Virginia

Your article states that the Battle of Kosovo lived on in Serbian literature and song as a symbol of the struggle against foreign domination. I am reminded of an old adage: "It's better to die on your feet than to live on your knees."

EVAN DALE SANTOS
Adelanto, California

Contact Us

Email ngsforum@ngm.com
Write National Geographic Magazine, PO Box 98199, Washington, DC 20090-8199. Include name, address, and daytime telephone. Letters may be edited for clarity and length.

GREEN EFFECT™

Winning Ideas for a Better World

SunChips® and National Geographic believe in the power of the Green Effect: If each of us takes one small step to make our community greener, we can create big change for our planet.

At SunChips, you can see it in the small steps taken every day to make snacks in a better way. Solar energy has already been harnessed to help make snacks in the Modesto, CA plant. They've dedicated energy to creating fully compostable packaging. SunChips is even helping to turn one tornado-devastated Kansas community into a model solar-powered eco-town.

All those "green steps" got us to thinking: Imagine what SunChips and National Geographic could do together to help people start their own personal Green Effect? What would they create, change, or reinvent?

To get the Green Effect movement started, we decided to award $20,000 each to five people or groups—such as a school, scout troop, green club, parents' organization, or church committee—with the most compelling, actionable ideas for green change.

The Green Effect challenge was on, and the response was incredible! In six weeks we received over 2,500 entries—each a great, green idea! More than 10,000 of your online votes determined one winner, and a panel of judges—each chosen for their involvement in the green community—picked the other four. Each winner received the funding to bring their idea to life. In addition, the five winners traveled to Washington, DC, to celebrate and share their projects with environmental leaders at National Geographic Society headquarters.

Turn the page and discover the small, imaginative steps people across the country are taking to create big change for our planet. You can learn more about the winners and see their videos at *greeneffect.com*—you just might even be inspired to create your own Green Effect.

"The Green Effect contestants give me tremendous hope. These are leaders who can and will lift us, community by community, out of the quagmire we've gotten ourselves into. It's time for a cultural shift and SunChips' philosophy is spot on."

–JAYNI CHASE, *Contest Judge*

Launch the Extreme Green Neighborhood Makeover

CarbonfreeDC.org WASHINGTON, DC

What better place to make a green statement than by helping lower-income families in our nation's capital? CarbonfreeDC will bring its Extreme Green Neighborhood Makeover to a city block in Washington, DC. The organization will use its award money to help 20 families green their homes and lifestyles by purchasing affordable carbon- and money-saving solutions such as CFL bulbs, programmable thermostats, weather stripping, low-flow showerheads, and Energy Star-rated appliances. Volunteers from the 650-person organization will help families install the green equipment. Eco-consultants will also donate their time to conduct energy audits of each home. By bringing its workshops about sustainability to the neighborhood, CarbonfreeDC plans to educate these families about energy efficiency, recycling, and growing organic food. The organization will publicize success stories to inspire other people to "get with the program."

Green Classroom Party Kits

Tricia Elisara with Julian Elementary School

JULIAN, CALIFORNIA

With 25 parties per year in most classrooms (multiplied by 14–21 classrooms per school), tons of disposable cups, plates, and cutlery end up in landfills. But Tricia Elisara and students at Julian Elementary School plan to change this by using their award money to create 100 Green Classroom Party Kits for each classroom. The washable plates, cups, and silverware will come in an easy-to-store, rolling container so kids can easily transport dirty dishes to the teachers' lounge or cafeteria to wash them. By employing this easily replicable idea, Tricia hopes 20 percent of the schools in San Diego County will follow Julian's example and start using similarly sustainable kits in their classrooms.

Re-tree Colorado

Tristan Frolich STEAMBOAT SPRINGS, COLORADO

The problem is complex. The mountain pine beetle has devastated over 1.5 million acres of lodgepole pines in Colorado. This loss leaves fewer trees to soak up carbon dioxide. Plus, the rotting dead trees give off methane, a greenhouse gas 20 times more destructive than CO_2. Tristan Frolich's plan, on the other hand, is simple: Plant more trees. Tristan is using his award to buy and plant 20,000 lodgepole pine and other saplings. "The beetle doesn't attack young trees, giving the forest a chance to rejuvenate," says Tristan. "By planting a variety of trees, we can minimize future outbreaks." And, by organizing a citywide family/community tree-planting day, he hopes to spur initiatives in neighboring communities. The cumulative results will be a giant leap forward in the fight against global warming, and help the Green Effect reach new heights.

"I was particularly glad to see that so many focused on how to educate and engage young people in changing our basic approach to how we live and on training people to think sustainably so they will carry the lessons and come up with their own ideas." –EDWARD NORTON, *Contest Judge*

Canal Tricycle Recycling Cooperative

Canal Youth Concilio SAN RAFAEL, CALIFORNIA

In San Rafael, CA, members of the Canal community don't have easy access to an effective recycling program. Because the community provides high-density, multi-family housing for many families, a lot of trash is produced, but very little is recycled. With its award money, the Canal Youth Concilio will purchase recycling bins for each apartment building and tricycles for collecting and transporting recycling. The plan will make it easier to educate members of the community about recycling, encourage people to ride bikes more often, and allow entrepreneurs in the neighborhood's recycling businesses to work more professionally and efficiently. These little steps will add up to big change in San Rafael. As one online voter lauded: "It is very important that our youth are doing something to protect and help the planet by first helping in the community! Five stars!"

ONLINE VOTING
GREEN EFFECT
WINNER

All We Are Saying...Is Give Plants a Chance!

Hingham High School

HINGHAM, MA

Hingham High School (HHS) wants to teach its children how plants and produce fit into a green lifestyle. HHS will use its award money to positively change the surrounding community and the environment. The greenhouse at HHS will give students the skills and knowledge to create "green" gardens, grow organic fruits and vegetables, prepare meals using their own produce—and appreciate the value of eating locally grown produce to reduce their carbon footprint and improve food quality. Their greenhouse will also be used for a student-run composting program and for growing and studying endangered local plant species. Beyond the impact on the 1,000+ student body, faculty, and community, every year's senior class would graduate with an "A" in appreciation for a green lifestyle, and the skills necessary to translate their green aspirations into attainable goals.

Growing Your Own Green Effect

"Big change starts with small steps" is the SunChips philosophy. And as you can see by the winners of the Green Effect, there is no shortage of people with great green ideas for making change happen. Let these winners inspire you so that the Green Effect spreads, and we all help to make the planet greener, better...happier. The next step is yours.

NATIONAL GEOGRAPHIC

OUR JUDGES:

JAYNI CHASE

Founder, Center For Environmental Education, eco-savvy mother of three, and wife of Chevy Chase

PHAEDRA ELLIS-LAMKINS

Chief Executive Officer, Green For All

DAVE HAFT

Group Vice President, Sustainability and Productivity, SunChips®/Frito-Lay

BOYD MATSON

Host, National Geographic Weekend, journalist

EDWARD NORTON

Actor, social and environmental activist

The reason so many Serbs feel vilified is evident from the way the Srebrenica massacre is still portrayed in the media. It has been 14 years since that event. The perpetrators have been largely identified and named. Their guilt is individual, and they are bearing the consequences. Modern society rejects the concept of collective guilt. To use language that implies that all ethnic Serbs are somehow responsible for the events in that Bosnian town a decade and a half ago is akin to blaming all Germans, past and present, for Auschwitz. Yet this behavior persists. It is doubtful that the majority of ethnic Serbs ever supported any such thing as the project of Greater Serbia. Furthermore, there is no implication that even those who did support such an idea supported ethnic cleansing, let alone participated in it.

STANISLAV STANKOVIC
Tampere, Finland

Divining Angkor

It always amazes me when I witness yet another beautiful wonder-of-the-world ruin. How were the rulers of these ancient civilizations able to get away with creating monuments to their gods, mortal coils, and palatial amusements while neglecting the basic needs of their people? Granted, Angkor created wealth with its elaborate system of water storage and distribution, but how many gods and goddesses must be depicted on their shrines and tombs at the expense of building a better infrastructure? The pyramids, Maya temples, churches of all faiths, and palaces of exquisite beauty serve only a fraction of the population, while most people must either labor or pay for the excesses of the priests, kings, and generals. Give us elaborate universities, hospitals, and museums instead of monuments and shrines to allay our fears of death.

MICHAEL STURDY
Armstrong, British Columbia

How were the rulers of these ancient civilizations able to get away with creating monuments to their gods, mortal coils, and palatial amusements while neglecting the basic needs of their people?

Among the guesses as to why Angkor's civilization collapsed, you mention "rapacious invaders, a religious change of heart, and a shift to maritime trade that condemned an inland city." You seem to think that a reasonable explanation is climatic change that caused the engineering works and dams to fail. An appropriate parallel is made with almost contemporary civilizations in Mesoamerica, which also failed because of changing patterns in the weather. May I suggest an additional idea? Growth and decadence are natural phenomena in history. Phases of growth in a civilization are always linked to high birthrates. Phases of low birthrates always anticipate decadence, lower economic standards of life, and loss of scientific knowledge. Natural high and low birthrates may help us understand history. This may even shed light on the situation of the world today.

ANGELO BERTOLO
Fiume Veneto, Italy

The hypothesis that the Khmer city of Angkor was abandoned at the end of a megadrought does not explain why the city was not repopulated after the end of the drought. Another possibility is that the Angkor water-management system provided an ideal habitat for the buildup of aquatic snail populations. These snails are intermediate hosts to many parasites, which might have built up to deadly concentrations for those who drank or entered the water. Since Angkor was a religious site and water was considered sacred, if the water turned deadly, it would be a sign of punishment from the deities in charge. Such a development could cause the religious system to crumble and create a taboo, in turn causing abandonment and preventing repopulation.

WALTER B. SIKORA
Athens, Georgia

In perusing the article on Ankgor and its demise, I was struck by the phrase: "When populations in countries exceed the carrying capacity of the land, real trouble begins." I see a similarity to our worldwide condition at present: Overpopulation, war, and the lack of food worldwide are approaching a climax, and we as a world community are blind to what we are doing.

DON BAILEY
Rigby, Idaho

LETTERS

In the early 1960s my parents went on a Pan Am around-the-world trip. The one sight my father could not forget was Angkor Wat. For years he wondered what happened to those beautiful ruins. He died without learning the answer. Now, ten years after his death, I picked up your July issue and finally learned the answer to his question.

BENJAMIN H. WEST
Galena, Ohio

Though I long to go to Angkor, insufficient finances, age (74 years), and health are deterrents. This article with its beautiful photographs has shown me around the place for free. But there is one omission: You ignore India's contribution to the restoration of the monuments.

M. R. RAJAGOPALAN
Tamil Nadu, India

Cosmic Vision

The article's opening page mentions that telescopes "will carry the eye to the edge of the universe." There is no edge to the universe. As long as people believe there is an edge, we'll waste money looking for it and continue letting people here on Earth starve.

ROBERT DAUBENSPECK
White River Junction, Vermont

Your article states the big bang was noisy! When did it go from theory to fact? I believe the world was created by God—and I looked at your pictures and said, "What a great creation."

EARL WARD
Bathurst, New Brunswick

Geography: Spread of the Amish

If you want to understand the spread of the Amish better, try driving a horse or pulling farm equipment through bumper-to-bumper traffic where 50 years ago grass grew in the middle of the road. My uncle grew up in Lancaster County, Pennsylvania, not more than 20 miles from where his ancestors settled in the early 1700s. He now has children in five states because of urban-sprawl-driven farmland prices and road congestion.

RUFUS BURKHOLDER
Fleetwood, Pennsylvania

On the "Spread of the Amish" map, I was surprised to find a dot on the north shore of Lake Huron—a new Amish community very close to our home. As I write this letter, hammers are pounding on the hill below our house, where an Amish family is building. When we retired here two years ago, we persuaded the seller to sever the house and woodlot from the farmland. He sold the unimproved land to our delightful Amish neighbors.

MARGARET HIBBARD
Iron Bridge, Ontario

Your article states that the Amish religion emphasizes "separation from the world." I am not Amish, but an Amish person explained to me that their philosophy is not about separation from the outside so much as community from within. Their denial of modern technology is based on the belief that automobiles and television draw individuals away from community and family.

JESSICA GOLDRING
Great Neck, New York

Technology: The Eyes Have It

You have an article on eyeglasses adjusted by pumping fluid between two lenses. About 50 years ago I read this exact idea in a science fiction novel. Now it has come to fruition.

BOB PATRICK
Everton, Arkansas

Flashback: Eyes on the Pies

The story on Automats brought back memories of childhood trips to that magical place. Imagine a secret little door that you put money in. You turn a knob, and out comes lunch. And before you leave, make yet one more trip to buy dessert. You had to sit at a table of strangers. We survived, we enjoyed, and now we remember those days of years ago.

RONALD REGEN
Rockaway, New Jersey

GeoPuzzle

You've marvelously combined my two top interests: geography and puzzles. I look forward to a GeoPuzzle in every issue.

MARC HERBERT
Walnut Creek, California

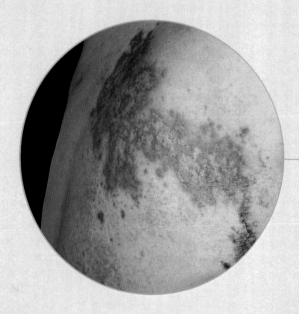

Patient Information about ZOSTAVAX® (pronounced "ZOS tah vax") Generic name: Zoster Vaccine Live

9815608

You should read this summary of information about ZOSTAVAX[1] before you are vaccinated. If you have any questions about ZOSTAVAX after reading this leaflet, you should ask your health care provider. This information does not take the place of talking about ZOSTAVAX with your doctor, nurse, or other health care provider. Only your health care provider can decide if ZOSTAVAX is right for you.

What is ZOSTAVAX and how does it work?

ZOSTAVAX is a vaccine that is used for adults 60 years of age or older to prevent shingles (also known as zoster).

ZOSTAVAX contains a weakened chickenpox virus (varicella-zoster virus).

ZOSTAVAX works by helping your immune system protect you from getting shingles. If you do get shingles even though you have been vaccinated, ZOSTAVAX may help prevent the nerve pain that can follow shingles in some people.

ZOSTAVAX may not protect everyone who gets the vaccine. ZOSTAVAX cannot be used to treat shingles once you have it.

What do I need to know about shingles and the virus that causes it?

Shingles is caused by the same virus that causes chickenpox. Once you have had chickenpox, the virus can stay in your nervous system for many years. For reasons that are not fully understood, the virus may become active again and give you shingles. Age and problems with the immune system may increase your chances of getting shingles.

Shingles is a rash that is usually on one side of the body. The rash begins as a cluster of small red spots that often blister. The rash can be painful. Shingles rashes usually last up to 30 days and, for most people, the pain associated with the rash lessens as it heals.

Who should not get ZOSTAVAX?

You should not get ZOSTAVAX if you:

- are allergic to any of its ingredients.
- are allergic to gelatin or neomycin.
- have a weakened immune system (for example, an immune deficiency, leukemia, lymphoma, or HIV/AIDS).
- take high doses of steroids by injection or by mouth.
- are pregnant or plan to get pregnant.

You should not get ZOSTAVAX to prevent chickenpox.

Children should not get ZOSTAVAX.

How is ZOSTAVAX given?

ZOSTAVAX is given as a single dose by injection under the skin.

What should I tell my health care provider before I get ZOSTAVAX?

You should tell your health care provider if you:

- have or have had any medical problems.
- take any medicines, including nonprescription medicines, and dietary supplements.
- have any allergies, including allergies to neomycin or gelatin.
- had an allergic reaction to another vaccine.
- are pregnant or plan to become pregnant.
- are breast-feeding.

Tell your health care provider if you expect to be in close contact (including household contact) with newborn infants, someone who may be pregnant and has not had chickenpox or been vaccinated against chickenpox, or someone who has problems with their immune system. Your health care provider can tell you what situations you may need to avoid.

What are the possible side effects of ZOSTAVAX?

The most common side effects that people in the clinical studies reported after receiving the vaccine include:

- redness, pain, itching, swelling, warmth, or bruising where the shot was given.
- headache.

The following additional side effects have been reported in general use with ZOSTAVAX:

- allergic reactions, which may be serious and may include difficulty in breathing or swallowing. If you have an allergic reaction, call your doctor right away.
- fever
- hives at the injection site
- joint pain
- muscle pain
- rash
- rash at the injection site
- swollen glands near the injection site (that may last a few days to a few weeks)

Tell your health care provider if you have any new or unusual symptoms after you receive ZOSTAVAX.

What are the ingredients of ZOSTAVAX?

Active Ingredient: a weakened form of the varicella-zoster virus.

Inactive Ingredients: sucrose, hydrolyzed porcine gelatin, sodium chloride, monosodium L-glutamate, sodium phosphate dibasic, potassium phosphate monobasic, potassium chloride.

What else should I know about ZOSTAVAX?

Vaccinees and their health care providers are encouraged to call (800) 986-8999 to report any exposure to ZOSTAVAX during pregnancy.

This leaflet summarizes important information about ZOSTAVAX.

If you would like more information, talk to your health care provider or visit the website at www.ZOSTAVAX.com or call 1-800-622-4477.

Rx only

Issued April 2009

[1]Registered trademark of Merck & Co., Inc.

Distributed by:
MERCK & CO., INC.
Whitehouse Station, NJ 08889, USA
20904745(6)(608)-ZOS-CON

Water Worlds A droplet framing a fish, a river teeming with people—water is the key to all life. It's also a building block for some great pictures. So take your best shot of the wet stuff, or document some different element, then send it our way. Every month this page features two photographs: one chosen by our editors, one chosen by our readers via online voting. For guidelines, a submission form, and more information, go to *ngm.com/yourshot.*

EDITORS' CHOICE

Debasis Roy Asansol, India

While transferring fish from one bowl to another, science tutor Roy, 27, was inspired. He composed this scene—a baby guppy sustained by a single droplet, cradled on a grass leaf atop a wooden stool—then put the fish back.

Alankar Chandra New Delhi, India

On his way to take a predawn bath in the holy city of Haridwar, Chandra, a 25-year-old business-school graduate, climbed a footbridge and captured a timeless sight: Hindu pilgrims spiritually purifying themselves in the sacred waters of the Ganges.

READERS' CHOICE

Taste a little richer.

Feel a little richer.

SAVE $1.00
on any TWO packages of
Keebler® Club® Crackers
(9 oz. or Larger, Any Flavor, Mix or Match)
Keebler
Light, Flaky, Buttery...
CLUB
CRACKERS
ORIGINAL
MANUFACTURER COUPON
EXPIRES NOVEMBER 30, 2009
5 30100 13133 0
0030100-014892
CONSUMER: LIMIT ONE COUPON PER PURCHASE OF PRODUCT INDICATED. VOID WHERE TAXED, RESTRICTED, OR PROHIBITED. CONSUMER MUST PAY SALES TAX. DEALER: We will reimburse you face value of this coupon plus $.08 handling if in accordance with Keebler coupon redemption terms: Copies available upon request. Mail properly redeemed coupons to: Keebler, P.O. Box 880274, El Paso, TX 88588-0274 Cash value 1/20 of $.01.
®, ™, © 2009 Kellogg NA Co. 62027361

A cracker that melts in your mouth? **Now that's rich.**

The Crasher

Melissa and Jackson Brandts (inset below) of Watertown, Minnesota, just wanted a memento of their trip to Canada's Banff National Park. Then a curious little creature changed everything. A ground squirrel scampering across the rocks was intrigued by their clicking camera and stopped to investigate. Jackson snapped a picture using the remote. After Melissa submitted the photo to Your Shot, it was chosen as one of our Daily Dozen favorites, posted on the *Geographic* website—and a furry star was born. The ground squirrel picture went viral on the Internet almost overnight. Pranksters digitally removed the animal from the lakeside and dropped it into famous photographs: The creature crashed scenes from the Beatles' *Sgt. Pepper* album portrait to an Apollo moonscape and taunted notables, including Tiger Woods and Abraham Lincoln. The Brandts also achieved their own celebrity, telling their story on television and to newspapers around the world. Will your vacation photo be the next big Internet sensation? Send it to us at *ngm.com/yourshot* and find out. *—Margaret G. Zackowitz*

Scene Stealer When they fired their camera's remote to get this ground squirrel in the picture, its autofocus function consigned Melissa and Jackson Brandts to a blurry background. **Turn the page for more animal images. ▸▸**

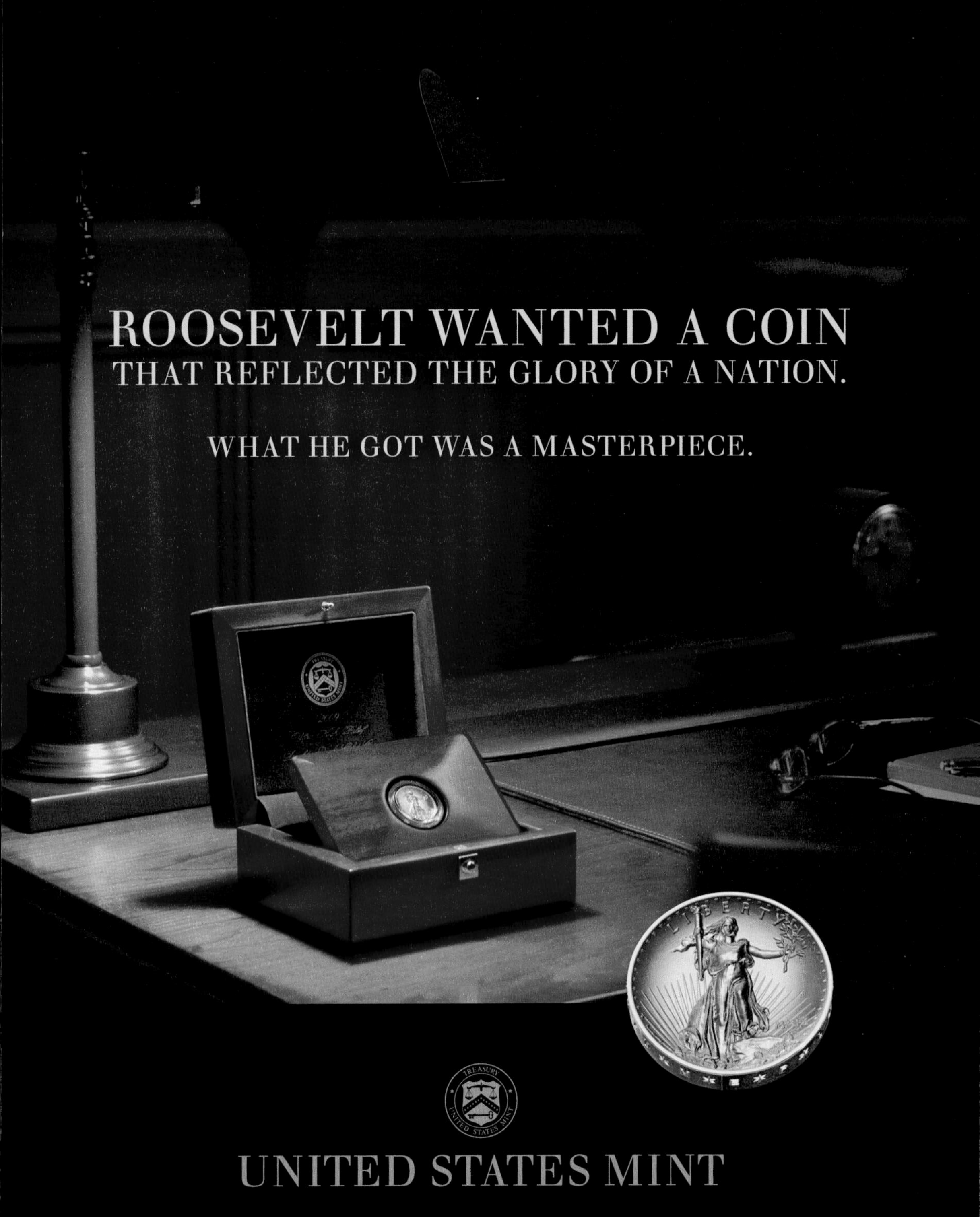
ROOSEVELT WANTED A COIN
THAT REFLECTED THE GLORY OF A NATION.
WHAT HE GOT WAS A MASTERPIECE.
LIBERTY
TREASURY
UNITED STATES MINT
UNITED STATES MINT
[The 2009 ULTRA HIGH RELIEF DOUBLE EAGLE GOLD COIN ~ by AUGUSTUS SAINT-GAUDENS]

Sanjay Upadhyay
Bangalore, India

Ashes the chimpanzee was born fuzzy but later lost all his hair. Visiting the Mysore Zoo, Upadhyay came across the naked animal. "He was sitting alone and looked sad," recalls Upadhyay, who works for a software company.

Andrew Wilson
Fall River, Massachusetts

A deer at the Buttonwood Park Zoo in New Bedford, Massachusetts, was untroubled that the leafy branch it was munching had flipped up to cover its eyes. Says Wilson, a Fall River city employee, "In a matter of minutes the leaves were consumed."

Sharon Fullingim Socorro, New Mexico

She'd seen the mantis by the hummingbird feeders before, but Fullingim, a sculptor, says she "didn't quite believe it would ever score lunch." The dry husk of the bird's body lay discarded beneath the feeder the next morning—and the bug was back at its perch, waiting for more.

ED VIESTURS
High-altitude mountaineer.
Eco-conscious philanthropist.
Summited the world's 14 tallest
peaks, without supplemental oxygen.
A man on a mission.
Obviously, he's not out of breath.
ROLEX. A CROWN FOR EVERY ACHIEVEMENT.
OYSTER PERPETUAL EXPLORER II
ROLEX
ROLEX.COM

Betty Berard Broussard
Coteau Holmes, Louisiana

The sky suddenly darkened and the rain came pouring down as Broussard, a retired state worker, photographed this owl near her home. "I hurriedly lifted the flash and took this photo," she remembers. The flash filled the owl's eyes with light in the gloom.

Morgan Ball
Lompoc, California

One damp night, says Ball, a biologist at Vandenberg Air Force Base, "I came across this little guy sitting right on the centerline." A friend drove his car to position the headlights behind the hopper, and Ball shot "from a toad's-eye view."

Erin Brotherton
Livonia, Michigan

Her car's sunroof was all that came between stay-at-home mom Brotherton and a carrot-seeking giraffe during a trip to an Ohio wildlife park.

Peter G. Allinson
Kingsville, Maryland

Andrew Armour, owner of a whale-watching business, swam with this young sperm whale off the coast of Dominica. The whale is so tame he comes when called, notes Allinson, a doctor who counts diving medicine among his specialties.

YOU
JUST
CAN'T
DOWNLOAD
THIS.
They say
life is an adventure.
Prove them right.
250 cities. 40 countries.
We know why you fly®
AmericanAirlines®
AA.com

oneworld

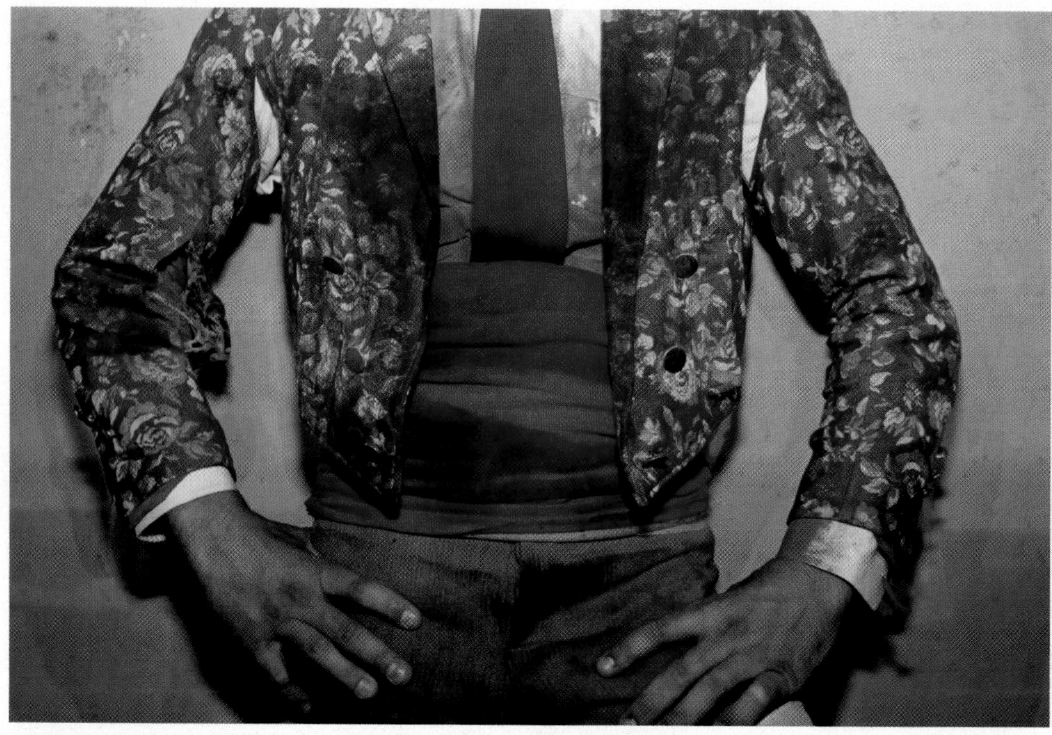

A proud *forcado* is bloodied but unbowed after a bullfight in Évora, Portugal.

More of Carlos Cazalis's work can be found at cazalis.org.

Brotherhood of the Bull Portuguese bullfighters belong to a unique tradition. For one thing, the bulls aren't killed in the ring. For another, some participants, called *forcados,* are amateurs. They're locals with day jobs, neighbors who cement their friendship in an ancient way: by risking their lives together. Their event is the *pega.* Eight men enter an arena, line up in single file, then try to subdue a charging bull by hand. They have no weapons, only each other to rely on. Every emotion is on naked display. There's something timeless about their bravery, something unifying about the beast. These bind them to antiquity and virility. Perhaps they're true descendants of the bull-vaulting Minoans. Certainly their way—their honor in the ring, their deeply cultivated sense of family outside it—is what I'd long been seeking.

Bullfighting is in my blood, but connecting with it, personally and artistically, has been a lifelong trial. I was born in Mexico, where my grandfather ran a plaza and my great-uncle was "El Calesero," a legendary matador. For years I photographed the sport professionally, but I couldn't see past the celebrity and corruption, or find any hidden authenticity. In 2003 I moved to Spain, hoping to shoot a series of intimate portraits of those involved in this controversial ritual. But it wasn't to be. Spanish matadors are cloaked in ego and machismo; they show little emotion. I began to wonder if my quest was quixotic. Then I learned of the forcados in Évora, Portugal. I've followed them for four years, and they're the real thing.

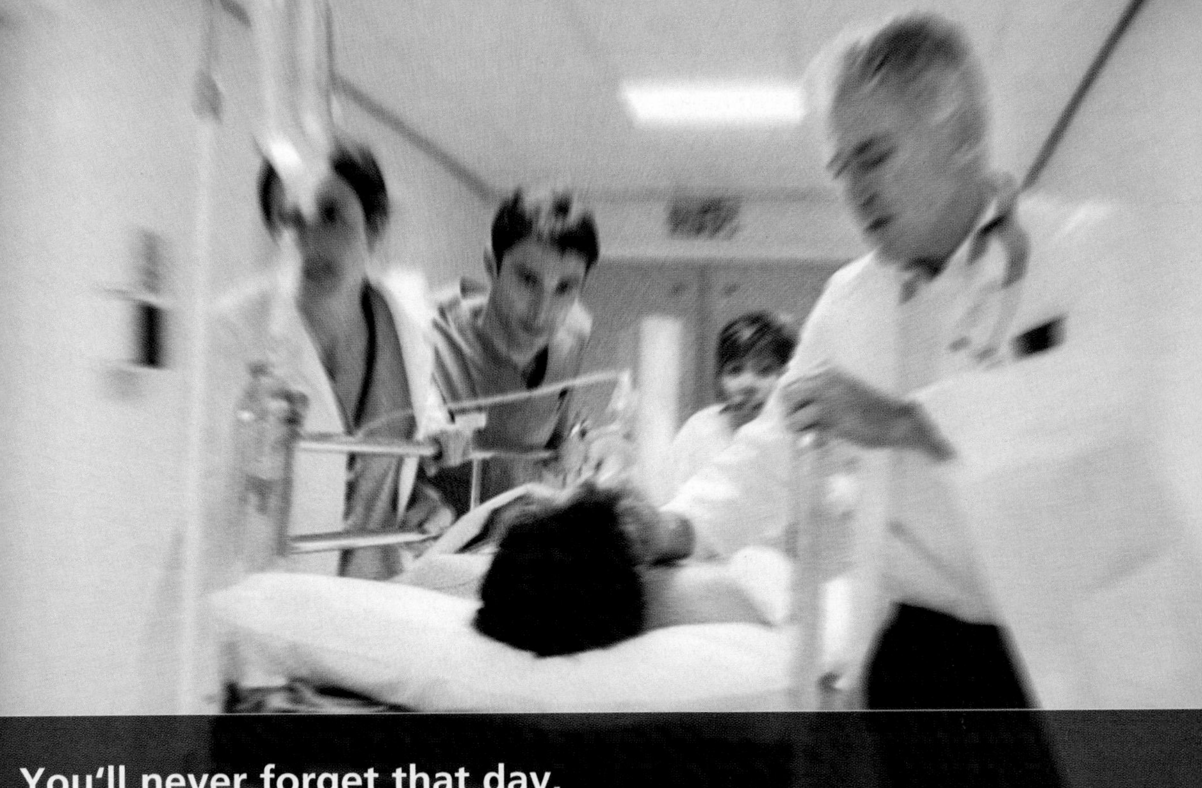

You'll never forget that day.

PLAVIX can help keep you from going through it again.

PLAVIX can help save lives for those who've had a heart attack caused by a completely blocked artery.

Without PLAVIX

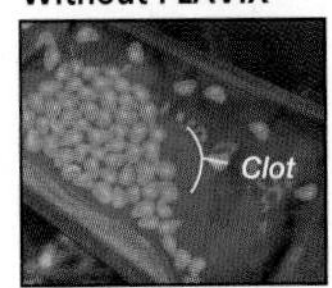

Clots that block off arteries are the main cause of heart attack. And now that you've had a heart attack you are at a greater risk of having another that can be fatal. That's why your doctor may put you on PLAVIX, along with your other heart medicines. Taking PLAVIX with your other heart medicines goes beyond what other heart medicines alone can do to keep blood platelets from sticking together and forming dangerous clots.

With PLAVIX

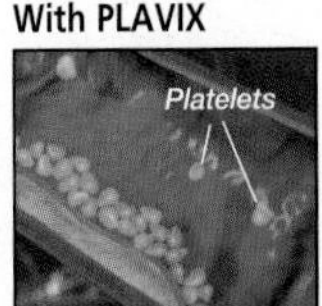

Important Safety Information: If you have a stomach ulcer or other condition that causes bleeding you should not use PLAVIX. Taking PLAVIX alone or with some other medicines including aspirin may increase bleeding risk. Tell your doctor before planning surgery or taking aspirin or other medicines with PLAVIX, especially if you've had a stroke. Some medicines that are used to treat heartburn or stomach ulcers, like Prilosec, may affect how PLAVIX works, so tell your doctor if you are taking other medicines. If fever, unexplained weakness or confusion develops, tell your doctor promptly. These may be signs of TTP, a rare but potentially life-threatening condition, reported sometimes less than 2 weeks after starting PLAVIX. Other rare but serious side effects may occur.

Ask your doctor how PLAVIX can help increase your protection against future heart attack, stroke, and even death.

To learn more about heart attacks and PLAVIX, visit www.plavix.com or call 1-877-920-1464.

You are encouraged to report negative side effects of prescription drugs to the FDA. Visit www.fda.gov/medwatch, or call 1-800-FDA-1088.

See important product information on the following pages.

If you need help paying for prescription medicines, you may be eligible for assistance. Call 1-888-4PPA-NOW (1-888-477-2669), or go to www.pparx.org

ONCE-A-DAY

Plavix®

(clopidogrel bisulfate) 75mg tablets

Protection that helps save lives.

sanofi aventis Bristol-Myers Squibb US.CLO.09.08.086/August 2009 264US09AB31715 sanofi-aventis U.S. LLC

PLAVIX **Rx Only**
(clopidogrel bisulfate) tablet, film coated

WHO IS PLAVIX FOR?

PLAVIX is a prescription-only medicine that helps keep blood platelets from sticking together and forming clots.

PLAVIX is for patients who have:

- had a recent heart attack.
- had a recent stroke.
- poor circulation in their legs (Peripheral Artery Disease).

PLAVIX in combination with aspirin is for patients hospitalized with:

- heart-related chest pain (unstable angina).
- heart attack.

Doctors may refer to these conditions as ACS (Acute Coronary Syndrome).

Clots can become dangerous when they form inside your arteries. These clots form when blood platelets stick together, forming a blockage within your arteries, restricting blood flow to your heart or brain, causing a heart attack or stroke.

WHO SHOULD NOT TAKE PLAVIX?

You should NOT take PLAVIX if you:

- are allergic to clopidogrel (the active ingredient in PLAVIX).
- have a stomach ulcer
- have another condition that causes bleeding.
- are pregnant or may become pregnant.
- are breast feeding.

WHAT SHOULD I TELL MY DOCTOR BEFORE TAKING PLAVIX?

Before taking PLAVIX, tell your doctor if you're pregnant or are breast feeding or have any of the following:

- gastrointestinal ulcer
- stomach ulcer(s)
- liver problems
- kidney problems
- a history of bleeding conditions

WHAT IMPORTANT INFORMATION SHOULD I KNOW ABOUT PLAVIX?

TTP: A very serious blood condition called TTP (Thrombotic Thrombocytopenic Purpura) has been rarely reported in people taking PLAVIX. TTP is a potentially life-threatening condition that involves low blood platelet and red blood cell levels, and requires urgent referral to a specialist for prompt treatment once a diagnosis is suspected. Warning signs of TTP may include fever, unexplained confusion or weakness (due to a low blood count, what doctors call anemia). To make an accurate diagnosis, your doctor will need to order blood tests. TTP has been reported rarely, sometimes in less than 2 weeks after starting therapy.

Gastrointestinal Bleeding: There is a potential risk of gastrointestinal (stomach and intestine) bleeding when taking PLAVIX. PLAVIX should be used with caution in patients who have lesions that may bleed (such as ulcers), along with patients who take drugs that cause such lesions.

Bleeding: You may bleed more easily and it may take you longer than usual to stop bleeding when you take PLAVIX alone or in combination with aspirin. Report any unusual bleeding to your doctor.

Geriatrics: When taking aspirin with PLAVIX the risk of serious bleeding increases with age in patients 65 and over.

Stroke Patients: If you have had a recent TIA (also known as a mini-stroke) or stroke taking aspirin with PLAVIX has not been shown to be more effective than taking PLAVIX alone, but taking aspirin with PLAVIX has been shown to increase the risk of bleeding compared to taking PLAVIX alone.

Surgery: Inform doctors and dentists well in advance of any surgery that you are taking PLAVIX so they can help you decide whether or not to discontinue your PLAVIX treatment prior to surgery.

Genetics: People with a specific genetic makeup may get less protection against future cardiovascular events, such as a heart attack or stroke, with Plavix.

WHAT SHOULD I KNOW ABOUT TAKING OTHER MEDICINES WITH PLAVIX?

You should only take aspirin with PLAVIX when directed to do so by your doctor. Certain other medicines should not be taken with PLAVIX. Be sure to tell your doctor about all of your current medications, especially if you are taking the following:

- aspirin
- nonsteroidal anti-inflammatory drugs (NSAIDs)
- warfarin
- heparin
- heartburn or stomach ulcer medicines, like Prilosec

Be sure to tell your doctor if you are taking PLAVIX before starting any new medication.

WHAT ARE THE COMMON SIDE EFFECTS OF PLAVIX?

The most common side effects of PLAVIX include gastrointestinal events (bleeding, abdominal pain, indigestion, diarrhea, and nausea) and rash. This is not a complete list of side effects associated with PLAVIX. Ask your doctor or pharmacist for a complete list.

HOW SHOULD I TAKE PLAVIX?

Only take PLAVIX exactly as prescribed by your doctor. Do not change your dose or stop taking PLAVIX without talking to your doctor first.

PLAVIX should be taken around the same time every day, and it can be taken with or without food. If you miss a day, do not double up on your medication. Just continue your usual dose. If you have any questions about taking your medications, please consult your doctor.

OVERDOSAGE

As with any prescription medicine, it is possible to overdose on PLAVIX. If you think you may have overdosed, immediately call your doctor or Poison Control Center, or go to the nearest emergency room.

FOR MORE INFORMATION

For more information on PLAVIX, call 1-800-633-1610 or visit www.PLAVIX.com. Neither of these resources, nor the information contained here, can take the place of talking to your doctor. Only your doctor knows the specifics of your condition and how PLAVIX fits into your overall therapy. It is therefore important to maintain an ongoing dialogue with your doctor concerning your condition and your treatment.

Distributed by:

Bristol-Myers Squibb/Sanofi Pharmaceuticals Partnership

Bridgewater, NJ 08807

CLO-BSCW-NGW-JUL09 Revised: July 2009

The next generation of forcados stares down a future foe in a Montemor-o-Novo ring. Each year features two Youth Days, one in this municipality, the other in Vila Franca de Xira. At both, group elders acquaint teens and preteens with cows and their ways. An early interest, aficionados say, is often predictive of a forcado-to-be.

At a house near Alcácer do Sal, forcados wrap themselves in traditional red sashes. The 40 men will share a light meal, then a culling process as the group leader, called the *cabo*, selects 16 for the night's match. Later, at the ring, he'll pick eight of those to face a bull.

No camera will store
as much as your heart.

Osa Peninsula

In the moments before a match, forcados pray in a farmhouse on the outskirts of Alcáçovas. After the bullfight a far more bacchanalian ritual begins. The group will go to a local tavern or home, then spend long hours toasting their friendship and analyzing their performance.

Following a match in Évora, costumed forcados meet and greet their supporters: friends, family, girlfriends, groupies. "Why do I date them?" one woman asked. "Because soccer and rugby players are boring by comparison." Most forcados are men 17 to 30 years old; few remain in the group once they marry.

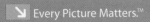

An Évora forcado springs into action as the *pega*, the second act, commences. The first part of a Portuguese bullfight features the *cavaleiro*, a horseman who weakens the bull by sticking it with spears called *bandarilhas*. The *cernelha*—two forcados fighting the bull but using tamer cattle as a distraction—can be used as a last resort.

Shadows of bleacher-seated spectators play on the outer wall of a plaza in Castro Marim. The bullfighting season in Portugal lasts from April through October, with hundreds of matches a year. Most attract several thousand attendees, though a soccer game can trim that figure if slated for the same evening.

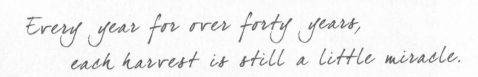

Everything comes to a head in Reguengos de Monsaraz, where the forcados bear the brunt. The man on the bull's horns is the *caras*, tasked with hanging on as long as possible. The one on the right is the *rabejador*, whose job is to get behind the animal and yank its tail, upsetting its equilibrium.

A bouquet of flowers, sure to be tossed into the ring at fight's end, rests in the wooden seats of an arena in Góis, a town in the Coimbra district. Pega enthusiasts throw objects—clothes, candies, dolls, hats—as tokens of luck and gratitude.

IMPORTANT FACTS

(LEER-i-kah)

IMPORTANT SAFETY INFORMATION ABOUT LYRICA

LYRICA may cause serious, even life threatening, allergic reactions.
Stop taking LYRICA and call your doctor right away if you have any signs of a serious allergic reaction:
- Swelling of your face, mouth, lips, gums, tongue or neck
- Have any trouble breathing
- Rash, hives (raised bumps) or blisters

Like other antiepileptic drugs, LYRICA may cause suicidal thoughts or actions in a very small number of people, about 1 in 500.
Call your doctor right away if you have any symptoms, especially if they are new, worse or worry you, including:
- New or worsening depression
- Suicidal thoughts or actions
- Unusual changes in mood or behavior

Do not stop LYRICA without first talking with your doctor.

LYRICA may cause swelling of your hands, legs and feet.
This swelling can be a serious problem with people with heart problems.

LYRICA may cause dizziness or sleepiness.
Do not drive a car, work with machines, or do other dangerous things until you know how LYRICA affects you. Ask your doctor when it is okay to do these things.

ABOUT LYRICA

LYRICA is a prescription medicine used in adults 18 years and older to treat:
- Pain from damaged nerves that happens with diabetes or that follows healing of shingles
- Partial seizures when taken together with other seizure medicines
- Fibromyalgia (pain all over your body)

Who should NOT take LYRICA:
- Anyone who is allergic to anything in LYRICA

BEFORE STARTING LYRICA

Tell your doctor about all your medical conditions, including if you:
- Have had depression, mood problems or suicidal thoughts or behavior
- Have or had kidney problems or dialysis
- Have heart problems, including heart failure
- Have a bleeding problem or a low blood platelet count
- Have abused prescription medicines, street drugs or alcohol in the past
- Have ever had swelling of your face, mouth, tongue, lips, gums, neck, or throat (angioedema)
- Plan to father a child. It is not known if problems seen in animal studies can happen in humans.
- Are pregnant, plan to become pregnant or are breastfeeding. It is not known if LYRICA will harm your unborn baby. You and your doctor should decide whether you should take LYRICA or breast-feed, but not both.

Tell your doctor about all your medicines. Include over-the-counter medicines, vitamins, and herbal supplements. LYRICA and other medicines may affect each other causing side effects. Especially tell your doctor if you take:
- Angiotensin converting enzyme (ACE) inhibitors. You may have a higher chance for swelling and hives.

BEFORE STARTING LYRICA, continued

- Avandia® (rosiglitazone)*, Avandamet® (rosiglitazone and metformin)* or Actos® (pioglitazone)** for diabetes. You may have a higher chance of weight gain or swelling of your hands or feet.
- Narcotic pain medicines (such as oxycodone), tranquilizers or medicines for anxiety (such as lorazepam). You may have a higher chance for dizziness and sleepiness.
- Any medicines that make you sleepy

POSSIBLE SIDE EFFECTS OF LYRICA

LYRICA may cause serious side effects, including:
- See "Important Safety Information About LYRICA."
- Muscle problems, pain, soreness or weakness along with feeling sick and fever
- Eyesight problems including blurry vision
- Weight gain. Weight gain may affect control of diabetes and can be serious for people with heart problems.
- Feeling "high"

If you have any of these symptoms, tell your doctor right away.

The most common side effects of LYRICA are:
- Dizziness
- Blurry vision
- Weight gain
- Sleepiness
- Trouble concentrating
- Swelling of hands and feet
- Dry mouth

If you have diabetes, you should pay extra attention to your skin while taking LYRICA and tell your doctor of any sores or skin problems.

HOW TO TAKE LYRICA

Do:
- Take LYRICA exactly as your doctor tells you. Your doctor will tell you how much to take and when to take it. Take LYRICA at the same times each day.
- Take LYRICA with or without food.

Don't:
- Drive a car or use machines if you feel dizzy or sleepy while taking LYRICA.
- Drink alcohol or use other medicines that make you sleepy while taking LYRICA.
- Change the dose or stop LYRICA suddenly. You may have headaches, nausea, diarrhea, or trouble sleeping if you stop taking LYRICA suddenly.
- Start any new medicines without first talking to your doctor.

NEED MORE INFORMATION?

- Ask your doctor or pharmacist. This is only a brief summary of important information.
- Go to **www.lyrica.com** or call **1-866-459-7422 (1-866-4LYRICA).**

Uninsured? Need help paying for Pfizer medicines? Pfizer has programs that can help. Call **1-866-706-2400** or visit www.PfizerHelpfulAnswers.com.

PARKE–DAVIS, Division of Pfizer Inc., New York, NY 10017

Version April 2009

* Avandia and Avandamet are registered trademarks of GlaxoSmithKline.
** Actos is a registered trademark of Takeda Chemicals Industries, Ltd., and is used under license by Takeda Pharmaceuticals of America, Inc., and Eli Lilly and Co.

Rx only

Switzerland Curiosity seekers stroll inside a crop circle etched in a Corcelles-près-Payerne wheat field in 2007. More than 200 feet in diameter, the pattern was spied by a Swiss military pilot flying over the Broye region.

PHOTO: SANDRO CAMPARDO, EPA/CORBIS

Cameroon At the Sanaga-Yong Chimpanzee Rescue Center, more than a dozen residents form a gallery of grief, looking on as Dorothy—a beloved female felled in her late 40s by heart failure—is borne to her burial.

PHOTO: MONICA SZCZUPIDER

Antarctica Radiating charisma on a 23°F morning, a three-foot-tall emperor penguin strikes a pose on the pack ice of the Amundsen Sea. The photographers were taking a month-long cruise aboard a Russian icebreaker.

Order prints of *National Geographic* photos online at **PrintsNGS.com.**

PHOTO: JONATHAN AND ANGELA SCOTT, NHPA/PHOTOSHOT

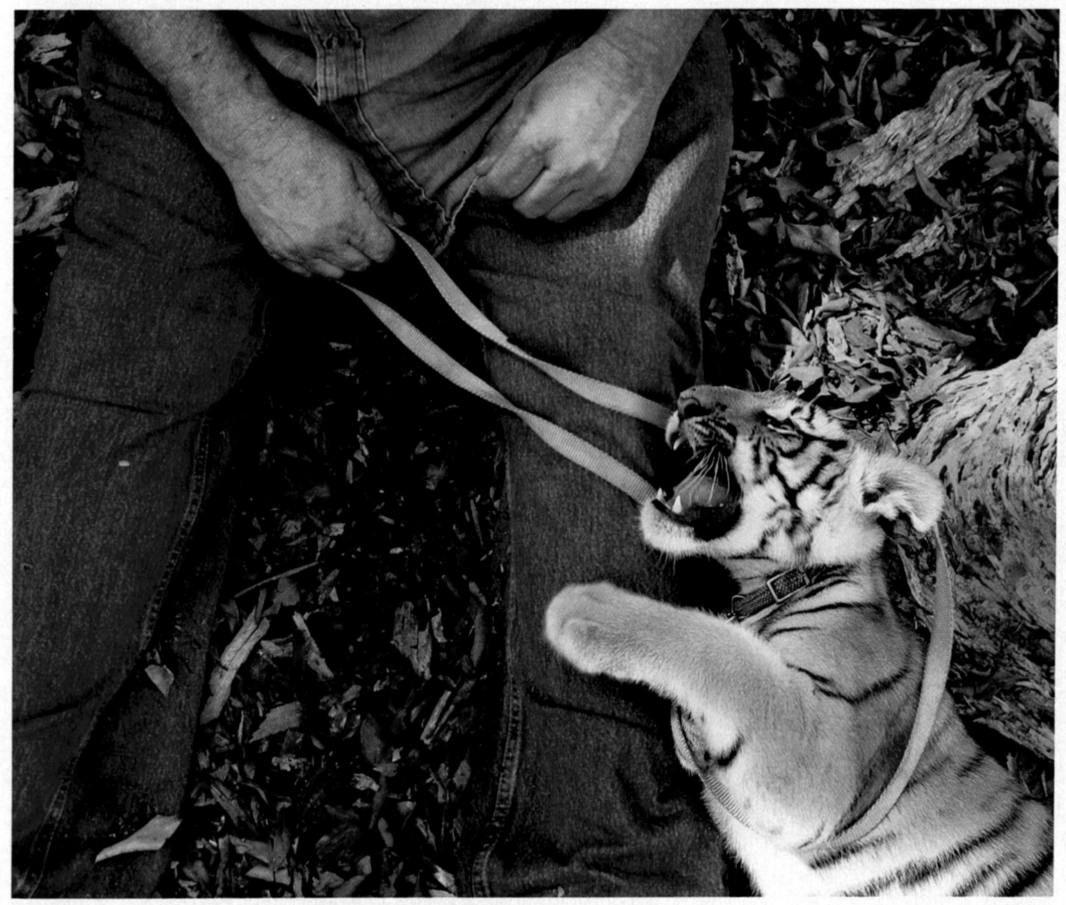

Floridian Vernon Yates charms kids when he shows them his cubs. Tiger experts deplore the practice.

A WORLD OF TIGERS
Privately held tigers far exceed wild ones. Zoos hold relatively few.

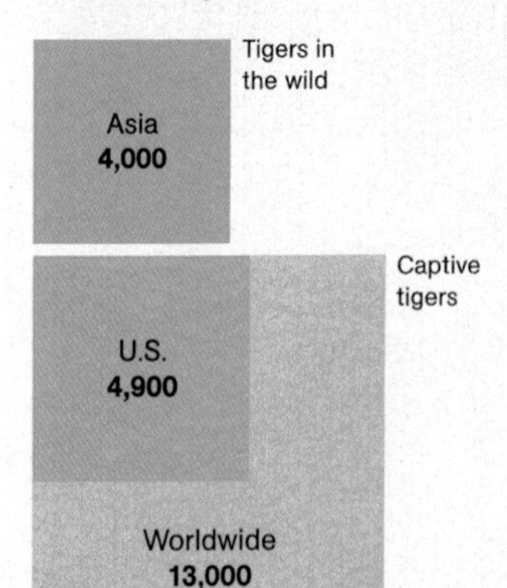

Don't Hold That Tiger

Vernon Yates took one of his 18 tigers to a party—his fee varies by event. "You can't trust tigers," a guest said. To prove her wrong, he told her he'd stick his head in the animal's jaws and tug its tongue for $20. She had to pay up.

The money goes to Yates's Wildlife Rescue and Rehabilitation shelter, licensed by Florida to take in animals in distress. "I deal with the true dirt of society," he says, telling of emaciated cats in squalid cages. He makes no apologies for his controversial style. He brings leashed cubs to schools for educational talks and takes his tigers on truck rides. Other rescuers are strictly hands-off. Contact can stress the animal and endanger humans, says Carole Baskin, a real estate investor who founded Big Cat Rescue, also in Florida. Indeed, between 1996 and 2008 the world's captive tigers killed at least 52 people and injured many more, from park guests to zookeepers.

One thing rescuers agree on: Cubs are cute, but a 500-pound cat with $7,500 yearly upkeep isn't an apt pet. More states are curtailing trade. But Louis Dorfman of the International Exotic Animal Sanctuary says, "There's always people who'll sell you a tiger." *—Marc Silver*

PHOTO: MAGGIE STEBER. GRAPHIC: OLIVER UBERTI, NG STAFF
SOURCE: RONALD TILSON AND PHILIP NYHUS, EDS., *TIGERS OF THE WORLD*, 2ND ED.

Flighty Oaks

In the National Arboretum's parched herbarium, where dried plants date to the 1790s, Alan Whittemore is providing needed acorn perspective. A year after few fell in parts of the U.S., the botanist says hungry squirrels and an anxious press—which breathlessly wondered, Is it climate change?—can relax.

Oak trees, he explains, don't have regular cycles or produce big harvests every year. Factor in weather—cold, wet springs impair pollination; hot, dry summers hinder maturation—and you've got acorn variability.

UCLA biologist Victoria Sork concurs. Back in the 1980s she tallied two near-zero years in eastern Missouri. The next fall? A bumper acorn crop. "We have to be careful about reading too much into one year," she says.

Meantime, says botanist Rod Simmons, the next boom year will be a boon year for all. One huge oak can drop up to 10,000 acorns, so well-fed squirrels are likely to hoard and forget their leftovers—and thus plant trees far and wide. *—Jeremy Berlin*

THE ACORN CYCLE
Oak species' acorn production can vary widely from year to year.

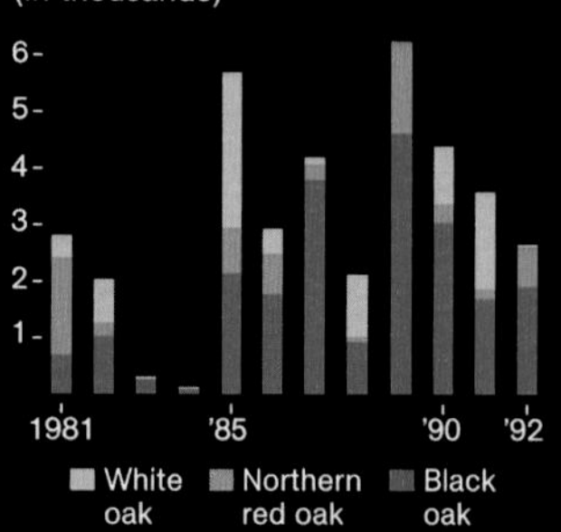

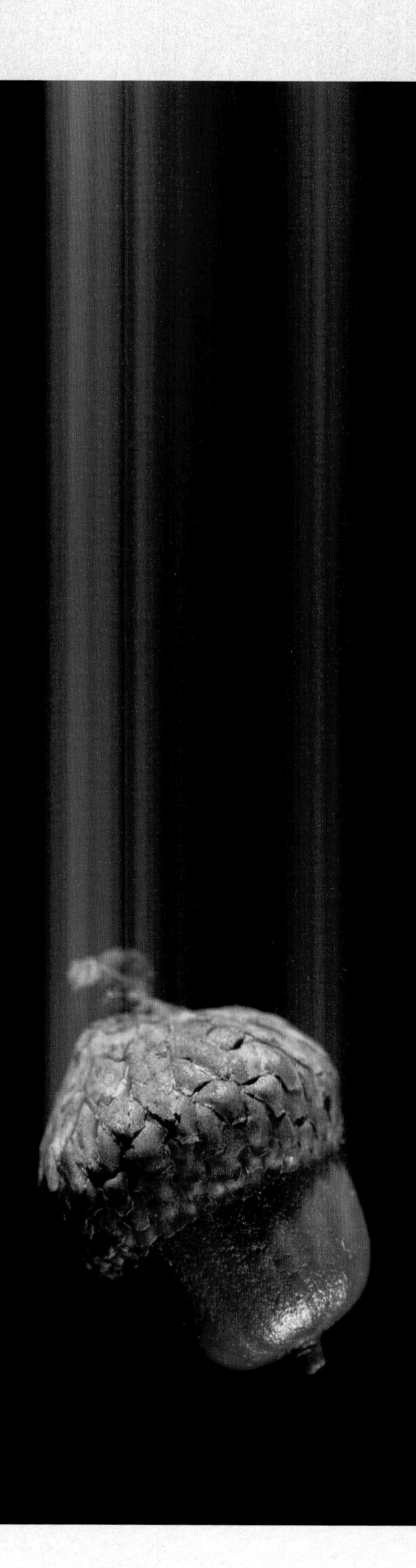

PHOTO: REBECCA HALE, NG STAFF. CHART: MINDY NICHAMIN. SOURCE: VICTORIA SORK, UCLA

advertisement

★★★★★ PASSPORT TO THE BEST ★★★★★

UNBELIEVABLE Vistas. UNLIMITED Rewards.

With the new Chase Sapphire℠ card, nothing will limit your travel experience. Stunning vistas are waiting to wow you, and the Chase Sapphire card makes traveling to them easier than ever.

The premier rewards program lets you earn points every time you use your Chase Sapphire card to make a purchase. Redeem points for virtually any reward you can think of—without expiration dates, blackout dates, or limits to what you can earn.

24/7 Dedicated Customer Service. Guaranteed. For direct access to an advisor, just call the number on the back of your Chase Sapphire card.

Use the Unlimited Rewards to Visit Unbelievable Vistas

Ultimate Grand Canyon 4-in-1 Helicopter Tour ★ Take the ultimate Grand Canyon tour! Helicopter from Las Vegas to the Grand Canyon, cruise the Colorado River, then spend time at the Canyon's West Rim and see the 360-degree panoramic views from the Skywalk.

Niagara Falls Luxury Tour ★ While you're visiting Niagara Falls, see both sides of the falls in style. Depart from either the American or Canadian side aboard the Maid of the Mist, your luxury tour includes a personal guide of the fall's best attractions.

Big Island Hawaii Volcano Adventure ★ See the lava fields on a comprehensive full-day tour of the Big Island's volcanoes. You'll explore Volcanoes National Park and the Big Island of Hawaii's lava flows and craters, and learn about the natural history of this amazing part of the world along the way.

New York Dinner Cruise ★ Enjoy a superb four-course dinner while you cruise the Hudson River and see Manhattan by night! Every table offers spectacular views of New York's breathtaking skyline, and dinner is served at your own private table.

advertisement

★ ★ ★ ★ ★ PASSPORT TO THE BEST ★ ★ ★ ★ ★

INTRODUCING THE CHASE SAPPHIRE℠ CARD

REWARDS THAT LET YOU TRAVEL **ANY** TIME. **ANY** PLACE.

Stonehenge, Salisbury, and Bath Day Trip ★ From famous Salisbury and Stonehenge to the beautiful Georgian city of Bath, you'll see it all on a cultural day trip from London. The tour includes travel by luxury coach and guided tours of Salisbury Cathedral, Stonehenge, and the Roman Baths.

San Francisco Bay Sunset Cruise ★ Take the ultimate sunset cruise, California-style! Relax as you enjoy amazing views of San Francisco and a hearty appetizer buffet from the famous Boudin Bakery during this casual cruise of San Francisco Bay.

Vancouver to Victoria and Butchart Gardens Tour ★ Cruise to Vancouver Island for a full day guided tour and find your way through the capital city of British Columbia. Spend the day exploring Victoria including world-famous Butchart Gardens.

Mt. Rainier Tour ★ Depart Seattle's urban world where breathtaking vistas await. You will enter the realm of this 14,000-foot mountain mass, whose lush forests, rocky peaks, and awe-inspiring views are the stuff of legend.

Muir Woods, Giant Redwoods, and Sausalito ★ Visit Muir Woods, whose towering giant redwoods, among the oldest and tallest on Earth, are one of the San Francisco Bay Area's great sights. The half-day tour also stops in picturesque Sausalito, nestled on the north shore of the Bay.

Lake Tahoe Photography Tour ★ See the "real Tahoe" on this private tour with a professional photographer who will point out Tahoe's best views. Whether it's wildflowers, raging waterfalls, or backcountry beauty, this photo tour will take you there.

Fantasia Snorkel Sea Safari ★ The Fantasia Snorkel Sea Safari is a world of fun for the whole family! Snorkel, slide, and rock climb all on this amazing 72-ft double deck catamaran, the only one of its kind in the Caribbean.

Gulfoss and Geysir Express ★ Take an afternoon tour from Reykjavik to experience geysers, waterfalls, and some of the most exciting natural phenomena in Iceland. In just six hours you'll visit the country's best known historical sites and natural wonders.

Log on to ***nationalgeographic.com/passporttothebest*** to find more ultimate vistas.

Web of Mystery Bushes, trees, an entire car shrouded in a ghostly white web—the sights last spring in the Dutch city of Rotterdam were like something from a horror film. People were "peering into the hedgerow expecting the mother of all spiders to emerge," says Stuart Hine, a British Natural History Museum entomologist. What was responsible for this spooky mess?

Not a giant, *Harry Potter*-esque arachnid, says Hine, head of a team that IDs mysterious bugs from around the world. The real culprits were the larvae of flying insects known as ermine moths, so named because their white wings with black spots resemble a certain weasel's winter coat. The caterpillars create these silky veils when they're trying to eat enough greenery to sustain themselves through weeks of cocooning and post-metamorphosis life as moths. Hine guesses that in the widely publicized Rotterdam incidents the bugs simply ran out of trees and randomly descended on a car (below). Weird as the giant webs can look, it's normal for these caterpillars to spin them. The larvae's feeding seldom causes lasting tree damage, and the adults are useful plant pollinators. And, Hine adds, "Once they're out of their cocoons, they're lovely little moths." —*Chris Carroll*

TAKEN WING
Several ermine moth species inhabit Europe. Hundreds more live elsewhere in the world.

After defoliating trees, caterpillars turned their attention to something less edible in Rotterdam, Netherlands.

PHOTOS: ARIE KIEVIT (ABOVE); ERIC LAGASA, WASHINGTON STATE DEPARTMENT OF AGRICULTURE (TOP). NGM MAPS

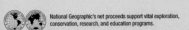

Apollo's Oven

In desert villages in Chile, 250 families are glad to let the sun roast their goat meat. The UN Development Programme paid $110 for the wood to build each solar oven. Fuel is free; pollution is nil. Women can spend time with kids instead of gathering wood. Solar Cookers International estimates one to two million solar ovens are now in villages, refugee camps, and sunny cities.

More are coming. This year Jon Bøhmer, a Norwegian living in Kenya, won a $75,000 "green" prize for devising a $7 version of a cardboard box oven (right) that can disinfect water and cook food. He's now working to distribute 10,000 equally cheap but more durable plastic ovens.

Skeptics might wonder if the sun can finish a dish. Ask Washington, D.C., pastry chef Michaela Borghese. She's honing her solar technique so she can do demos in the developing world. After an hour in the HotPot, with no stirring, her polenta (below) was creamy and delicious. And you should taste her buttery solar linzer torte. *—Marc Silver*

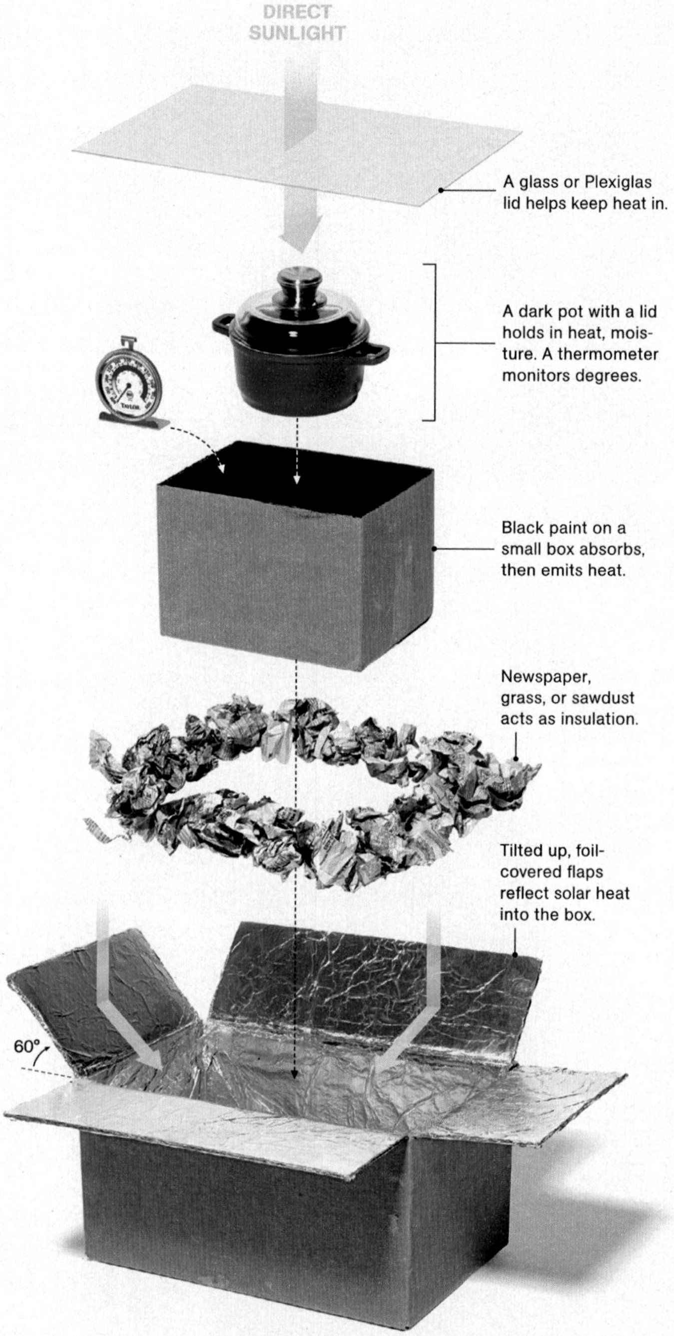

DIRECT SUNLIGHT

A glass or Plexiglas lid helps keep heat in.

A dark pot with a lid holds in heat, moisture. A thermometer monitors degrees.

Black paint on a small box absorbs, then emits heat.

Newspaper, grass, or sawdust acts as insulation.

Tilted up, foil-covered flaps reflect solar heat into the box.

60°

◀ **BUY IT**

With aluminum panels and a black pot in a glass bowl, the HotPot (left) can hit 300°F. Its retail price is about $100. In poor areas, Solar Household Energy subsidizes a $40 HotPot with cardboard reflectors.

▲ **BUILD IT**

A no-frills solar box oven, a favorite of do-it-yourselfers since the 1970s, is easy to assemble. This one hit and held 195°F on a mostly sunny June day—more than enough heat to pasteurize water.

PHOTOS: REBECCA HALE, NG STAFF

Qat Goes Global Grab a bitter leaf and chew. Then take another and another, letting the wad rest in your cheek. Soon you'll feel less hungry, more alert, a little euphoric. That's qat (pronounced cot, often spelled khat), a stimulant used for centuries in Yemen and Africa's Horn by laborers for energy and by men to while away afternoons. Today, with increased urbanism, easier access to cash, and relaxed social mores, it's taking deeper root. "People chew it in the early morning, on the street," says psychologist Michael Odenwald. "Children and breast-feeding women chew it."

Qat's fanning out too, flown daily to African and Yemeni expats in Europe, Australia, and North America while also entering Uganda and Rwanda. With greater demand and better transport—which gets qat to market in 48 hours, while it's still fresh and potent—farmers are planting more of the profitable, easy-to-grow crop. In Yemen, the cultivated area has increased more than tenfold since 1970; in Ethiopia, qat has become a top foreign-exchange earner.

The plant's spread raises concerns, though. In Yemen, it's irrigated from shrinking aquifers. In Somalia, Odenwald has seen abuse linked to mental-health problems. And in the West, countries have debated whether to leave the leaf legal, like tobacco, or ban it, like marijuana. Qat will get you arrested in the U.S., Canada, and much of Europe. In the U.K., for now, it's perfectly fine. *—Karen E. Lange*

STIMULATING DEBATE
A stem of qat (above) is bundled with others (below) to become an international commodity—and a controversial drug.

A seller in Hargeysa, Somaliland, offers enough qat for an afternoon of chewing. The price: $10.

PHOTOS: PASCAL MAITRE (ABOVE); REBECCA HALE, NG STAFF (TOP)

Your World MasterCard® comes with rewards, offers and perks that matter to you. Whether it's tee time reservations at premier golf courses or preferred seats at the big game, you decide what's in your perfect world. Offers may vary. Go to priceless.com/world and register for more details.

Offers are illustrative. Actual offers may vary. Terms and conditions apply. Go to priceless.com/world and register for more details.

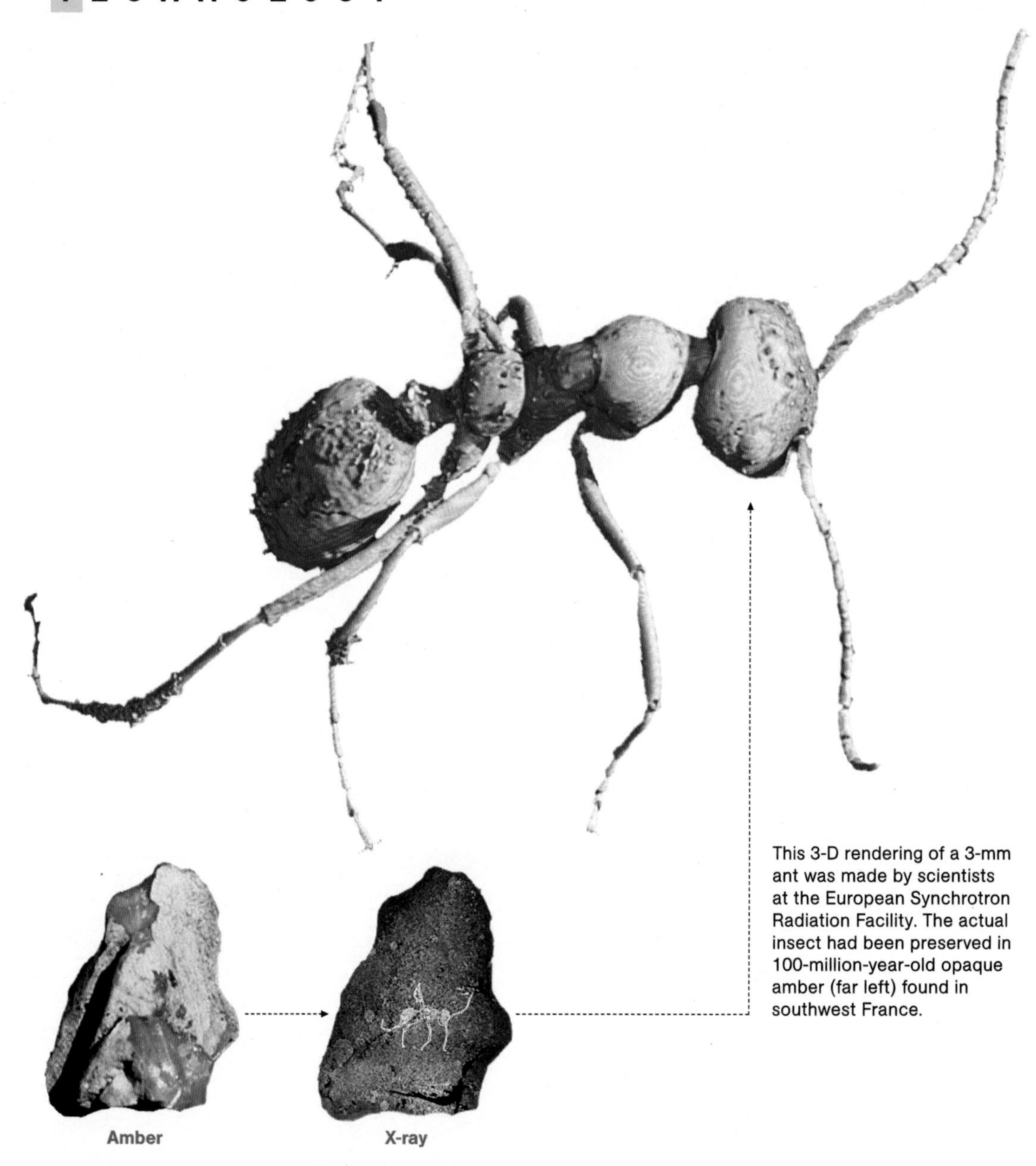

This 3-D rendering of a 3-mm ant was made by scientists at the European Synchrotron Radiation Facility. The actual insect had been preserved in 100-million-year-old opaque amber (far left) found in southwest France.

X-ray Marks the Spot

Problem: Amber is great at preserving fossils from key paleontological periods like the Cretaceous, when bugs boomed and dinosaurs disappeared, but the ancient tree sap can be so opaque that the treasures within are hidden.

Solution: Synchrotron imaging, an x-ray technique more powerful than CT scanning and more precise than grindstone cutting. Over three years, French paleontologists Malvina Lak, Paul Tafforeau, and colleagues have used a synchrotron to sift through 25 pounds of 100-million-year-old amber and find 1,000 fossils, including wasps, flies, and spiders. An x-ray beam penetrates the rock-like drippings and pinpoints the encased specimens, which the team builds up as computerized models and produces in 3-D plastic form.

Bonus: Paleontologists, who have been known to guard their precious samples, may now start sharing the virtual wealth. *—Jeremy Berlin*

PHOTOS: PAUL TAFFOREAU AND MALVINA LAK, ESRF/CNRS

GIGABYTES OR HORSEPOWER?

HOW DO YOU JUDGE THE NEXT GENERATION OF AUTOMOBILES?

HELLO SOMEDAY

THE FIRST-EVER HS HYBRID.

Physically, philosophically, it is impossible to fully assess the HS Hybrid using only an antiquated measuring stick, like horsepower. Indeed, there is a new kind of power in the HS, and it's not just confined to the engine.

HORSEPOWER
Power and efficiency come together in the fourth and latest hybrid from Lexus, the new HS 250h, delivering 187 total system horsepower and 35 EPA MPG combined rating.*
20+ Computers:
GIGABYTES
Power and efficiency come together in over 20 available onboard computer systems in the HS, which monitor, assist and help improve driver experience.
Total System Horsepower: 187
Electric / 40HP
Gasoline / 147HP
Get the whole story at lexus.com/hs.

*2010 EPA MPG Estimates 35/34/35 City/Highway/Combined. Actual mileage will vary. Vehicle shown with optional equipment. ©2009 Lexus.

Mercurial Loons

Mercurial Loons Why are some loons acting so, well, loony? Mercury. Long-term studies of common loons in the United States and Canada reveal that the toxic stuff is invading birds' brains and bodies in dangerous concentrations. It's disrupting behavior and physiology—and could put loon populations in peril.

Mercury is a naturally occurring metal, but industrial activities like coal burning emit more than double nature's share. In waterways mercury can turn into the even more insidious methylmercury and infiltrate the food chain, its potency building at each level. Loons, which eat contaminated fish, are among the harder hit species.

Conservation biologist David Evers and colleagues report that loons with high methylmercury levels lay smaller eggs (left), forage less often, and spend less time nesting—leading to 41 percent fewer fledged chicks. Another study shows highly toxic loons produce no chicks. Birds may also grow abnormal wing feathers, impeding flight.

Of course, loons aren't alone: Methylmercury affects many fish-eaters, from otters to eagles to humans. Asks Evers, "If loons are in trouble, how will we fare?" —*Jennifer S. Holland*

PEOPLE AT RISK

As industry grows worldwide, so does human exposure to methylmercury. Some U.S. states now regulate emissions, for good reasons.

- **Every year, one in ten** fetuses, or about 400,000, is exposed to dangerous methylmercury levels in the womb, where the poison is more concentrated than in maternal blood.
- **Methylmercury exposure** can affect IQ and lead to neurological damage and behavioral problems.
- **High-level exposure** has been linked to mental retardation and symptoms of cerebral palsy.

Loons affected by mercury are less likely to piggyback their chicks.

PHOTOS: ARTHUR MORRIS, CORBIS (ABOVE); DANIEL POLESCHOOK, JR., AND GINGER GUMM (TOP)

A typical ride on Munich's urban wave lasts about a minute.

Hanging *Zehn*

On a summer Saturday, surfers line up within sight of a city bus stop for a shot at riding a wave. Yet this is Bavaria, in Germany; the nearest ocean is 400 miles away. So where are they going? Here on Munich's Eisbach stream, the surf is always up.

The Eisbach wave is artificial. Concrete blocks, placed under the water to calm the river a bit as it emerges from an underground channel, form a permanent three-foot swell as the water rushes up and over them. The water is only four feet deep, but the current can slam surfers into the concrete-lined banks with a force comparable to a nine-foot ocean wave.

Riding the wave is officially verboten. That may change soon if city authorities add surfboards to ordinances governing boats. Though police chased surfers off when they discovered the Eisbach in the 1970s, these days the swell is an institution. Cops turn a blind eye. Tourists far outnumber surfers, often taking pictures from the bridge above. "It's unique that someone can surf in the middle of the city," says surfer Maik Dengel. "It's Munich's own little curiosity." *—Andrew Curry*

PHOTO: PETER KNEFFEL, PICTURE-ALLIANCE/DPA. NGM MAPS

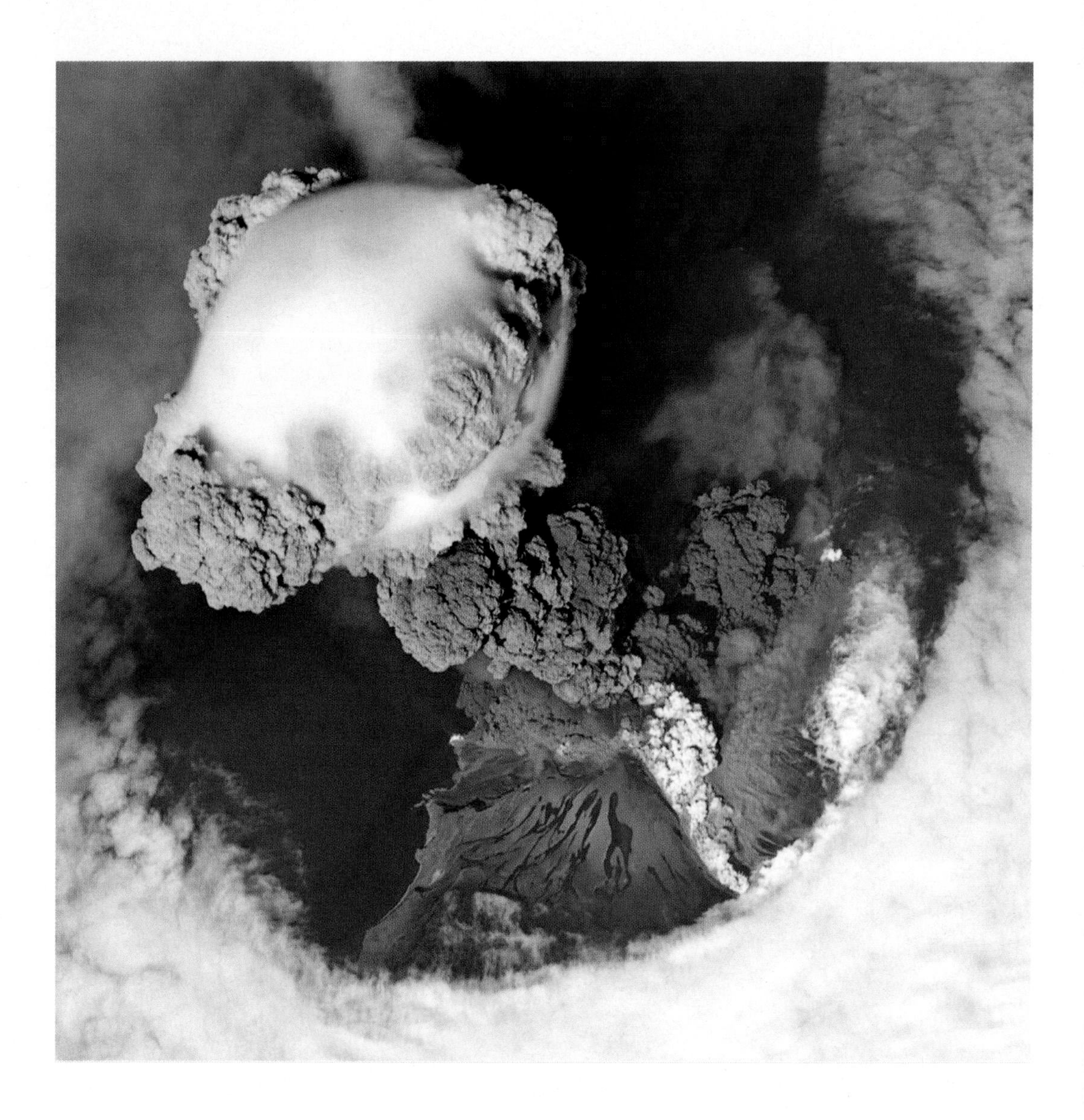

Erupting periodically since 1760, Sarychev Peak is now one of the Kuril Islands' most active volcanoes.

Sarychev Goes Boom A hot fist of steam and ash punches through the cloud cover above the Sarychev volcano on Matua Island, part of the remote Kuril Islands chain off Russia and Japan. Crew members on the International Space Station captured this image on June 12, 2009, soon after the mountain burst open. Over three days the ash column topped 50,000 feet, diverting air travel as debris and sulfur dioxide belched skyward.

The smooth white cap atop the plume is likely a pileus cloud—a transient puff of condensation that forms when a climbing air mass cools above an ash column. But the cloud peephole is an enigma. It may have resulted from the eruption's shock wave, or from evaporation as air sank and warmed around the plume. Or perhaps it was simply a lucky window onto the epic blast. *—Jennifer S. Holland*

PHOTO: IMAGE SCIENCE AND ANALYSIS LABORATORY, NASA/JOHNSON SPACE CENTER

Ahoy, Reindeer The antlered animals weren't made for this—to stumble onto a boat in the middle of an autumn night (below) and bump and sway on the water for six hours until they attain solid ground again and resume their overland migration to a winter refuge. In Norway, both reindeer and their seminomadic herders, members of the indigenous Sami, are struggling to find their balance as development intrudes on traditional grazing lands, changing the way humans and animals move.

For centuries the Sami have seasonally driven reindeer between grassy feeding grounds on the coast and lichen-rich tundra in the interior. Unlike the tiny wild population to the south, the 250,000 northern reindeer are semidomesticated, raised principally for the sale of their meat. The income helps support about 3,000 herders, nowadays a small fraction of Norway's Sami population of 50,000.

But no longer can herds drift as easily as clouds. A glut of holiday cabins, oil and gas complexes, military ranges, windmill farms, and power lines has fragmented migration corridors. To adapt, the Sami are shifting grazing areas and using boats as well as trucks to maneuver herds. With the loss of pastureland, some worry that the culture's long dependence on reindeer will slowly vanish, destined for tales told by elders. *—Tom O'Neill*

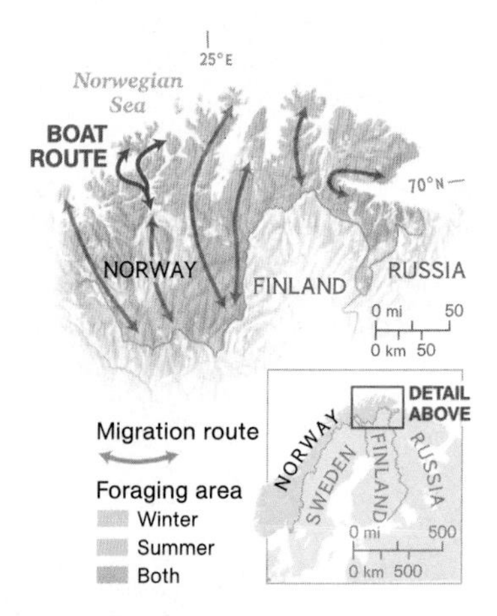

Migration of Norwegian reindeer by land and sea may take more than a week and cover over 120 miles.

To skirt development, some of Norway's reindeer now migrate partly by boat, in packs of 600 or so.

PHOTO: BENJAMIN DRUMMOND. NGM MAPS. SOURCES: INTERNATIONAL CENTRE FOR REINDEER HUSBANDRY; NORWEGIAN REINDEER HUSBANDRY ADMINISTRATION

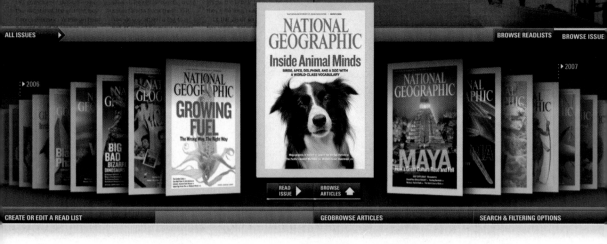

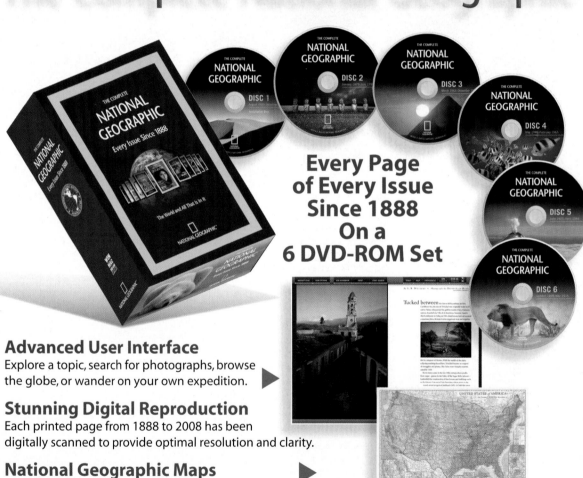

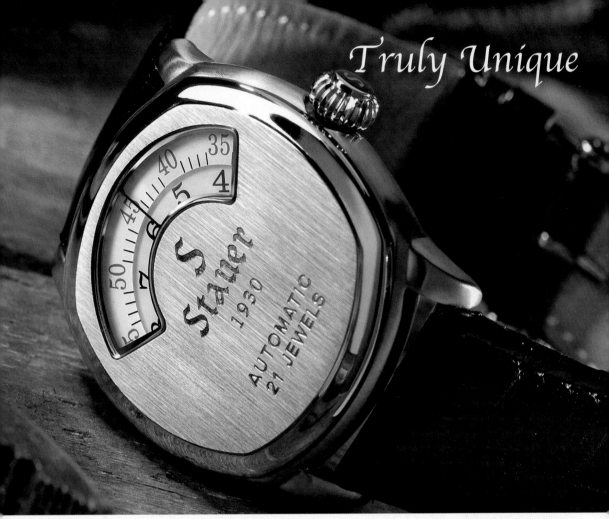

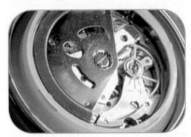

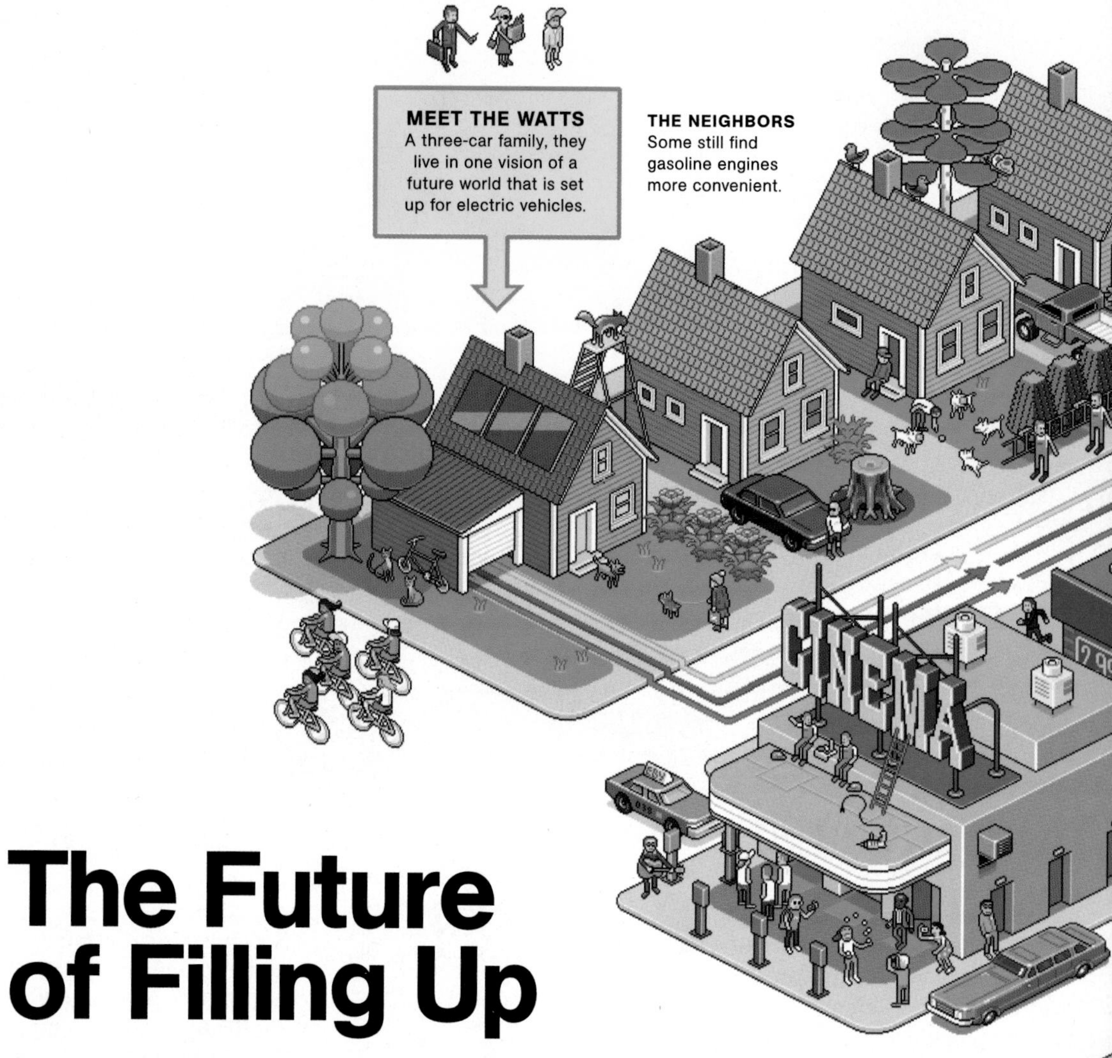
MEET THE WATTS
A three-car family, they live in one vision of a future world that is set up for electric vehicles.
THE NEIGHBORS
Some still find gasoline engines more convenient.
CINEMA

The Future of Filling Up

This time around, electric cars may play even in Peoria. But they will require a new infrastructure to replace today's filling stations—one that dispenses electrons rather than gasoline.

In the future most cars will run on electricity from sun, wind, and water. Plug-in electric vehicles will hum along streets, giving off no exhaust. Oil imports and greenhouse gas emissions will fall. Smog will lift. At least that's the vision many people are hoping will become reality. But first there are a few logistical problems to work out, including this one: Just where are all these revolutionary new cars going to plug in?

Between 2010 and 2012, car manufacturers are planning to introduce dozens of models that are either partially or completely powered by rechargeable batteries. Plug-in hybrid vehicles like the Chevy Volt, which will have a gasoline engine to fall back on after about 40 miles, will take up to eight hours to charge on ordinary 120-volt household current; some all-electric vehicles, with larger batteries designed to provide a range of 100 to 200 miles, will need 10 to 12 hours. Many homes have 240-volt outlets (used to run clothes dryers) that could in principle cut the time in half, and much charging can be done overnight, when

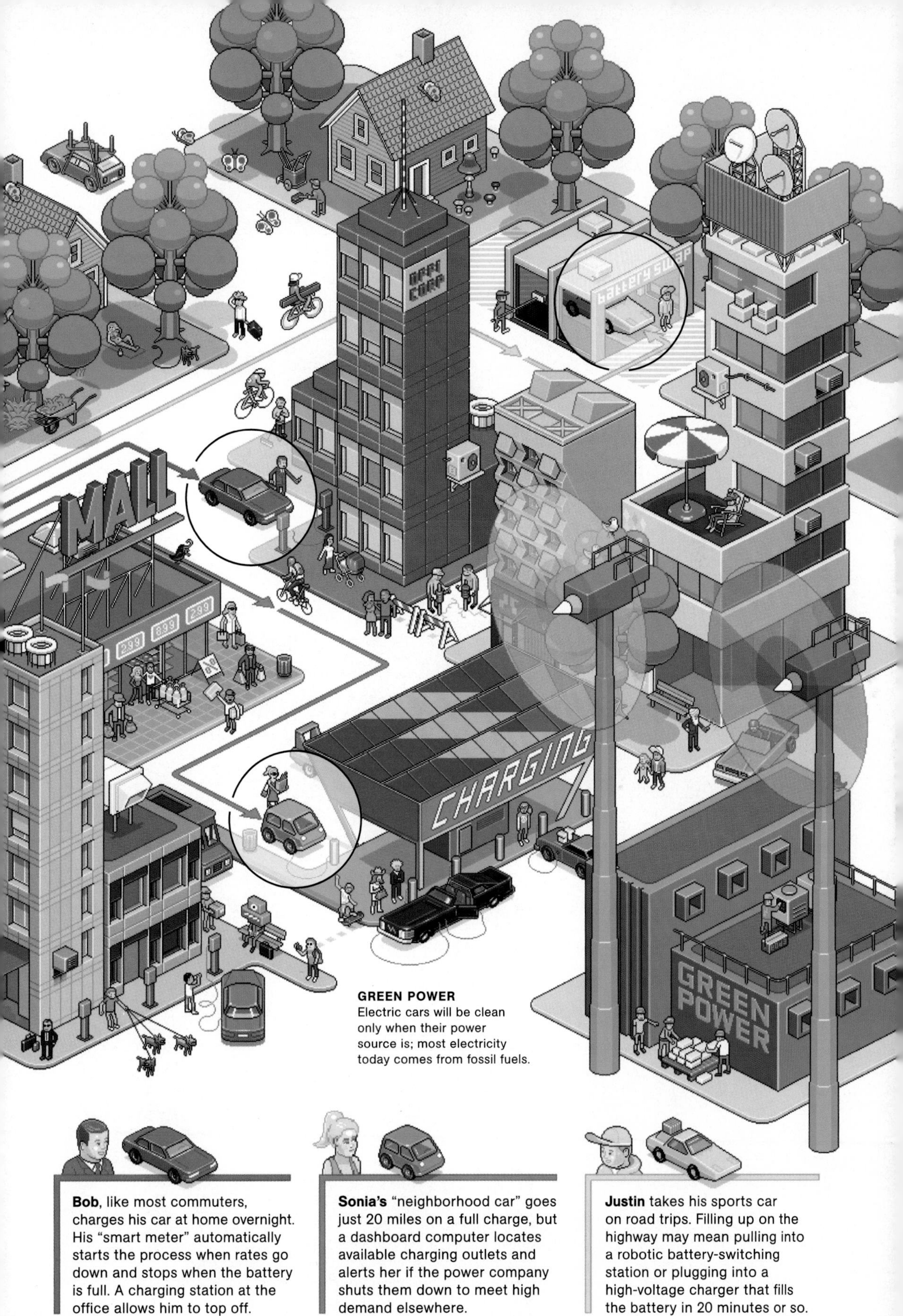

GREEN POWER
Electric cars will be clean only when their power source is; most electricity today comes from fossil fuels.

Bob, like most commuters, charges his car at home overnight. His "smart meter" automatically starts the process when rates go down and stops when the battery is full. A charging station at the office allows him to top off.

Sonia's "neighborhood car" goes just 20 miles on a full charge, but a dashboard computer locates available charging outlets and alerts her if the power company shuts them down to meet high demand elsewhere.

Justin takes his sports car on road trips. Filling up on the highway may mean pulling into a robotic battery-switching station or plugging into a high-voltage charger that fills the battery in 20 minutes or so.

ART: EBOY. SOURCES: ART JAMES, OREGON DEPARTMENT OF TRANSPORTATION; TIM LIPMAN, UNIVERSITY OF CALIFORNIA, BERKELEY; RICHARD LOWENTHAL, COULOMB TECHNOLOGIES; BRIAN PURCHIA, OFFICE OF THE MAYOR, SAN FRANCISCO

intel
CORE i7
inside
Look for
Intel
Inside®

THE
COMPUTER
IS PERSONAL
AGAIN.
hp

hp

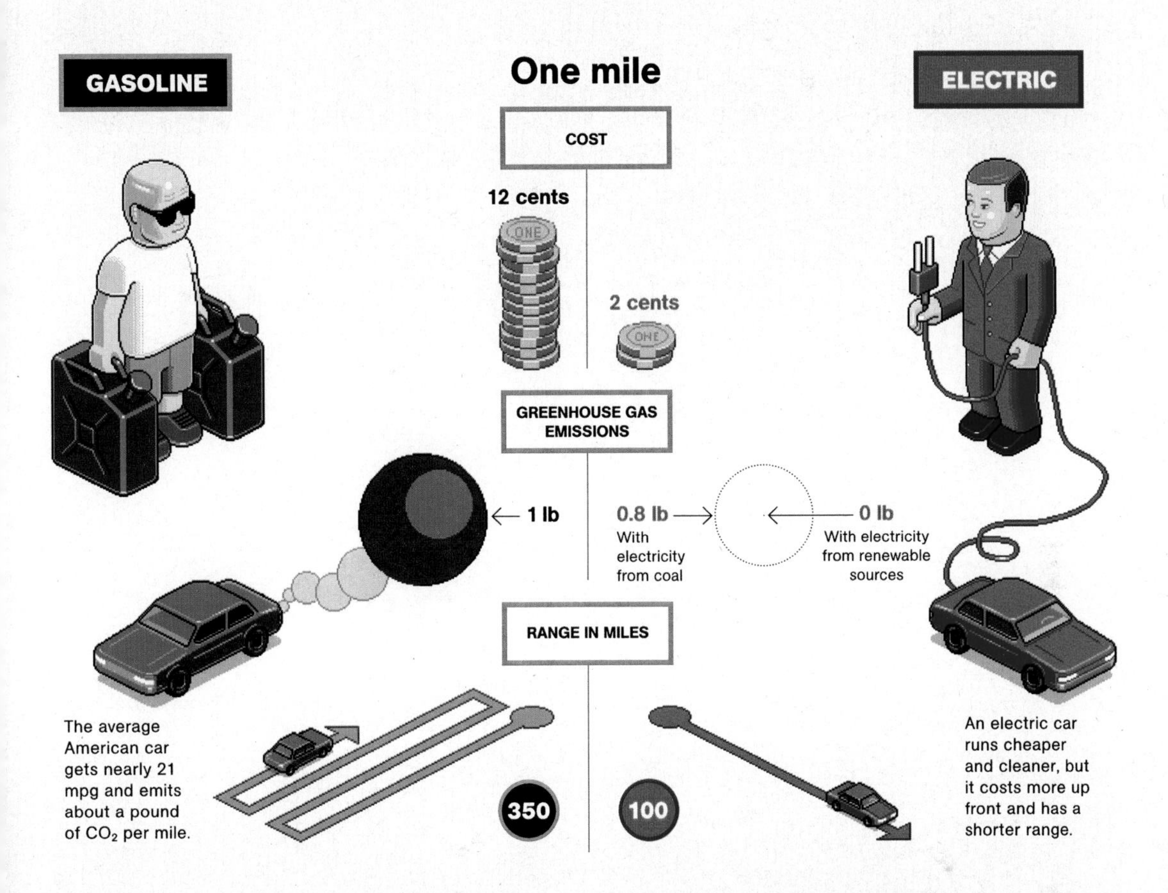

The average American car gets nearly 21 mpg and emits about a pound of CO_2 per mile.

An electric car runs cheaper and cleaner, but it costs more up front and has a shorter range.

electricity is relatively cheap. Still, in order for lots of people to adopt electric cars, there will have to be a network of charging stations—places where apartment dwellers, commuters who want to top off at work, and highway travelers can plug in. "You don't want to put out too much infrastructure if you don't have the vehicles," says Art James of the Oregon Department of Transportation. "But you won't get the vehicles until you have the infrastructure."

That infrastructure is starting to emerge in scattered places around the world, especially where governments are encouraging it. In Israel, a country with expensive gasoline and short driving distances, a California-based company called Better Place has constructed more than a thousand charging stations; next year it hopes to begin building a similar network in the San Francisco area. Under the Better Place plan, the company owns and tracks the use of the expensive lithium-ion batteries in its subscribers' cars; they pay a fee to recharge, even when they're recharging at home. That lowers the cars' initial cost by a third or more, but customers must buy from manufacturers that have agreed to use Better Place's standard batteries; so far only Renault-Nissan has signed on. To allow extended highway travel, Better Place will also build switching stations where robots swap out drained batteries for charged ones in a few minutes.

Alternatively, the future may look more like the present, with drivers of any brand of car able to pull into any brand of service station. Coulomb Technologies, another California start-up, claims it could build high-speed, 480-volt charging stations that would allow highway travelers to fill up in 20 minutes—about the time it takes for a rest stop. With 117,000 gas stations in the United States today and fewer than 500 charging stations, many not even open to the public, the scale of the transition to an electric-car world is daunting. But so are high gasoline prices and a warming climate. Says James, "It's going to happen quicker than you think." *—Karen E. Lange*

ART: EBOY. SOURCES: ART JAMES, OREGON DEPARTMENT OF TRANSPORTATION; TIM LIPMAN, UNIVERSITY OF CALIFORNIA, BERKELEY; U.S. DEPARTMENT OF ENERGY

EGYPTIAN MUSEUM, CAIRO

Animals Everlasting

Wrapped in linen and reverently laid to rest, animal mummies hold intriguing clues to life and death in ancient Egypt.

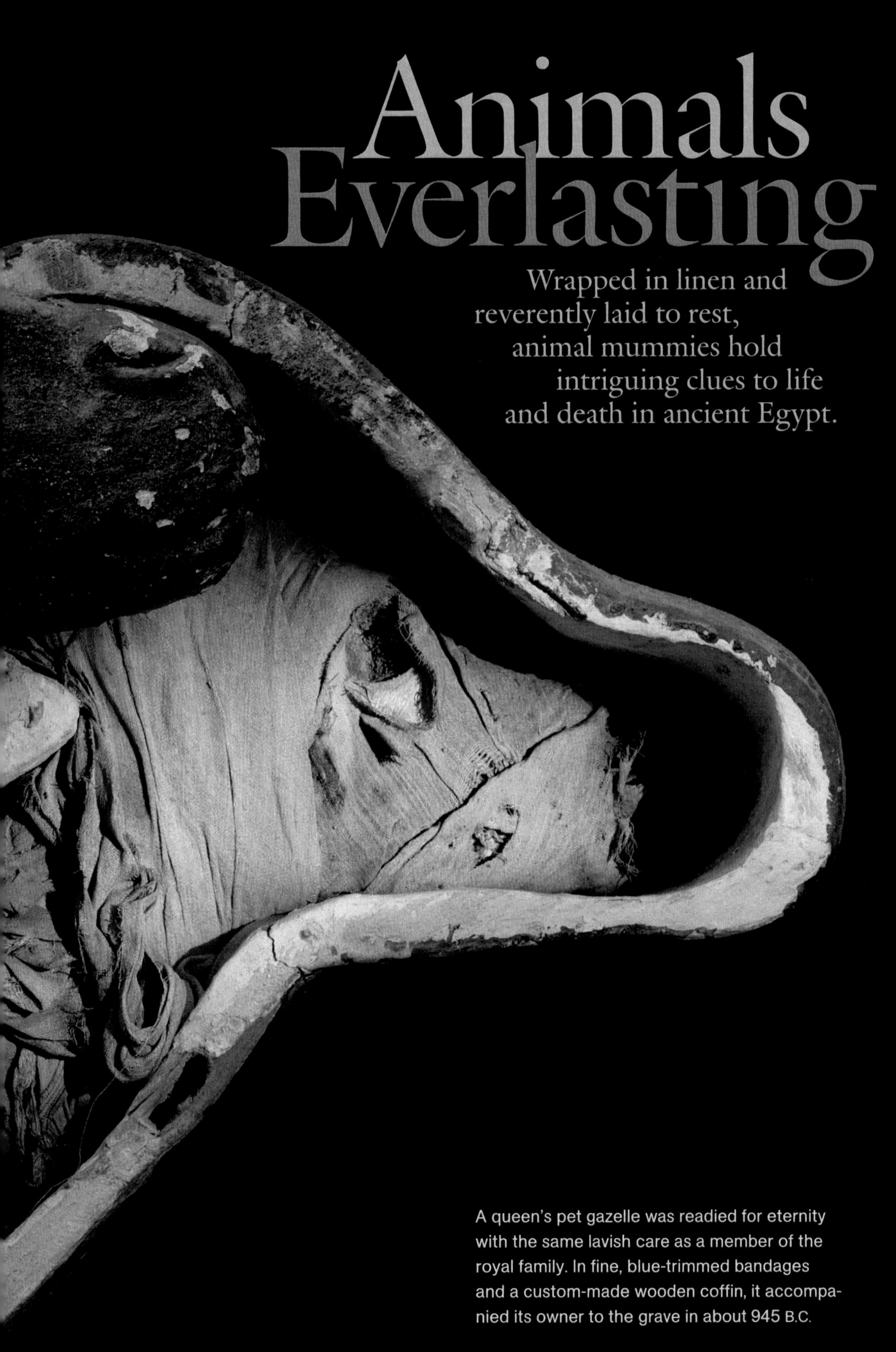

A queen's pet gazelle was readied for eternity with the same lavish care as a member of the royal family. In fine, blue-trimmed bandages and a custom-made wooden coffin, it accompanied its owner to the grave in about 945 B.C.

BY A. R. WILLIAMS

PHOTOGRAPHS BY RICHARD BARNES

In 1888 an Egyptian farmer digging in the sand near the village of Istabl Antar uncovered a mass grave. The bodies weren't human. They were feline—ancient cats that had been mummified and buried in pits in staggering numbers. "Not one or two here and there," reported the *English Illustrated Magazine*, "but dozens, hundreds, hundreds of thousands, a layer of them, a stratum thicker than most coal seams, ten to twenty cats deep." Some of the linen-wrapped cats still looked presentable, and a few even had gilded faces. Village children peddled the best specimens to tourists for change; the rest were sold in bulk as fertilizer. One ship hauled about 180,000, weighing some 38,000 pounds, to Liverpool to be spread on the fields of England.

Those were the days of generously funded expeditions that dredged through acres of desert in their quest for royal tombs and for splendid gold and painted masks and coffins to adorn the estates and museums of Europe and America. The many thousands of mummified animals that turned up at sacred sites throughout Egypt were just things to be cleared away to get at the good stuff. Few people studied them, and their importance was generally unrecognized.

In the century since then, archaeology has become less of a trophy hunt and more of a science. Excavators now realize that much of their sites' wealth lies in the multitude of details about ordinary folks—what they did, what they thought, how they prayed. Animal mummies are a big part of that pay dirt.

"They're really manifestations of daily life," says Egyptologist Salima Ikram. "Pets, food, death, religion. They cover everything the Egyptians were concerned with." Specializing in zooarchaeology—the study of ancient animal remains—Ikram has helped launch a new line of research into the cats and other creatures that were preserved with great skill and care. As a professor at the American University in Cairo, she adopted the Egyptian Museum's languishing collection of animal mummies as a research project. After taking precise measurements, peering beneath linen bandages with x-rays, and cataloging her findings, she created a gallery for the collection—a bridge between people today and those of long ago. "You look at these animals, and suddenly you say, Oh, King So-and-So had a pet. I have a pet. And instead of being at a distance of 5,000-plus years, the ancient Egyptians become people."

Today the animal mummies are one of the most popular exhibits in the whole treasure-filled museum. Visitors of all ages, Egyptians and foreigners, press in shoulder to shoulder to get a look. Behind glass panels lie cats wrapped in strips of linen that form diamonds, stripes, squares, and crisscrosses. Shrews in boxes of carved limestone. Rams covered with gilded and beaded casings. A gazelle wrapped in a tattered mat of papyrus, so thoroughly flattened by mummification that Ikram named it Roadkill. A 17-foot, knobby-backed crocodile, buried with baby croc mummies in its mouth. Ibises in bundles with intricate appliqués. Hawks. Fish. Even tiny scarab beetles and the dung balls they ate.

Some were preserved so that the deceased

Pampered in a temple during its lifetime, a sacred baboon was enshrined after death in the Tuna el-Gebel catacombs. Priests prayed and made offerings to it there as signs of their abiding reverence.

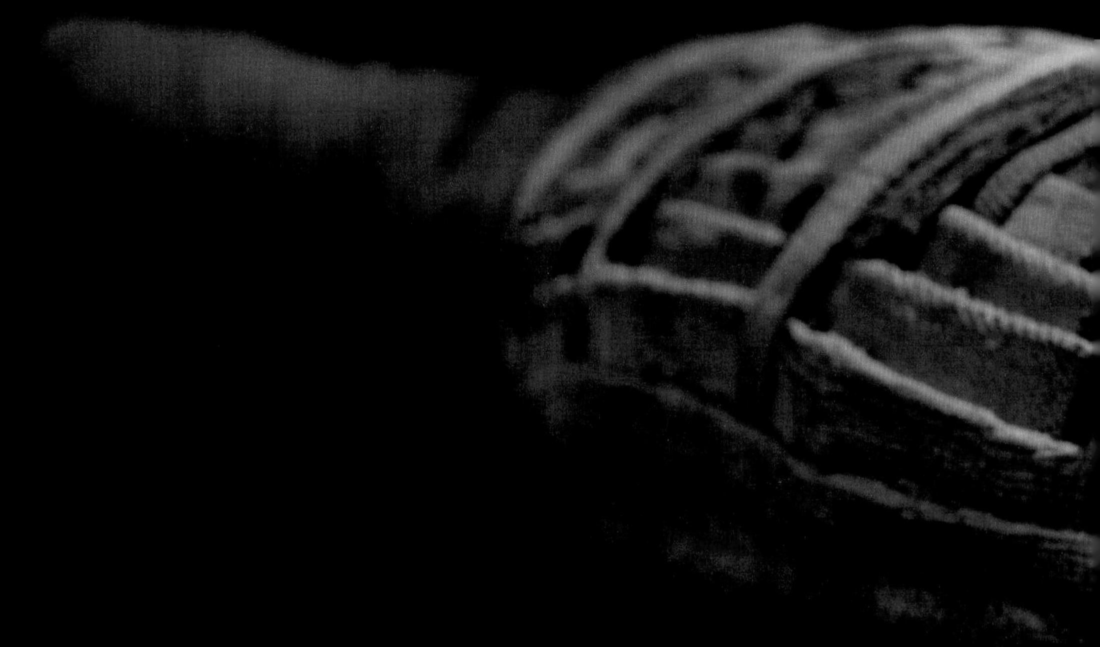

Votive mummies, each buried with a prayer, are infinitely varied but not always what they seem. Counterclockwise from top: A cunning crocodile is a fake—it has nothing inside. A coffered linen bundle conceals an ibis. A shrew on a tiny stone coffin identifies the contents precisely. Papyrus and linen trace the contours of a gazelle. A raptor with an appliquéd face holds only a few bones.

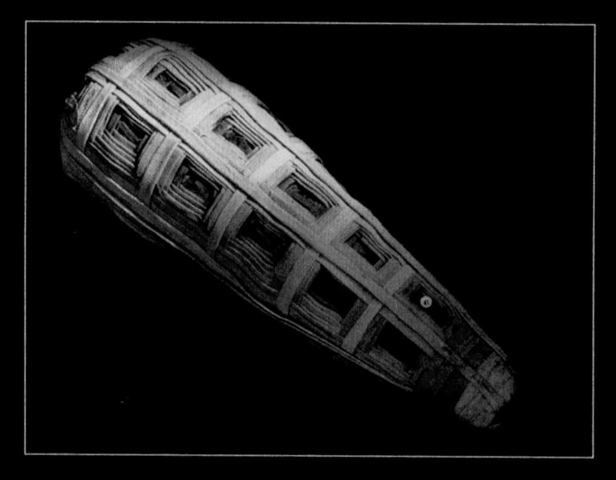

EGYPTIAN MUSEUM; AGRICULTURE MUSEUM, CAIRO (GAZELLE MUMMY)

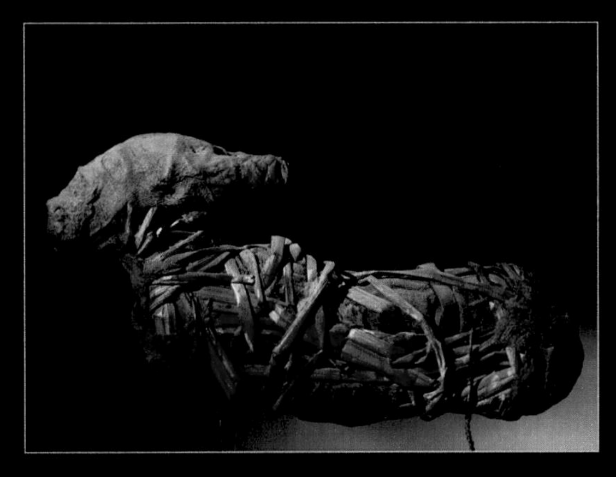

Meat mummies on display at the Egyptian Museum in Cairo were prepared as a royal picnic for the afterlife. Ducks, legs of beef, ribs, roasts, and even an oxtail for soup were all dried in natron, bound in linen, and packed in a reed basket for burial in a queen's tomb.

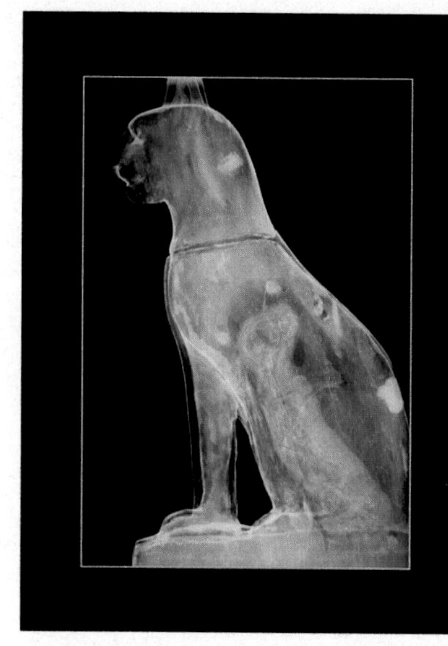

The innermost secrets of mummies at the Egyptian Museum have emerged in a recent study. A wooden, cat-shaped coffin (opposite, at right), plastered and whitewashed to imitate limestone, stands about 14.5 inches tall, dwarfing the kitten inside (x-ray, left). Spiral wrappings and a painted mask conceal a grown cat—one of countless thousands buried as votive offerings in the sands of Istabl Antar.

would have companionship in eternity. Ancient Egyptians who could afford it prepared their tombs lavishly, hoping that their assembled personal items, and everything shown in specially commissioned works of art, would magically be available to them after death. Beginning in about 2950 B.C., kings of the 1st dynasty were buried at Abydos with dogs, lions, and donkeys in their funerary complexes. More than 2,500 years later, during the 30th dynasty, a commoner at Abydos named Hapi-men was laid to rest with his small dog curled at his feet.

Other mummies were provisions for the dead. The best cuts of beef, succulent ducks, geese, and pigeons were salted, dried, and wrapped in linen. "Victual mummies" is what Ikram calls this gourmet jerky for the hereafter. "Whether or not you got it regularly in life didn't matter because you got it for eternity."

And some animals were mummified because they were the living representatives of a god. The venerable city of Memphis, the capital for much of Egypt's ancient history, covered 20 square miles at its largest in about 300 B.C., with a population of some 250,000. Today most of its crumbled glory lies under the village of Mit Rahina and the surrounding fields. But along a dusty lane, the ruins of a temple stand half hidden amid tufts of grass. This was the embalming house of the Apis bull, one of the most revered animals in all of ancient Egypt.

A symbol of strength and virility, the Apis was closely linked to the all-powerful king. He was part animal, part god and was chosen for veneration because of his unusual set of markings: a white triangle on his forehead, white winged patterns on his shoulders and rump, a scarab silhouette on his tongue, and double hairs at the end of his tail. During his lifetime he was kept in a special sanctuary, pampered by priests, adorned with gold and jewels, and worshipped by the multitudes. When he died, his divine essence was believed to move on to another bull, and so a search for the new one began. Meanwhile, the body of the deceased was transported to the temple and laid on a bed of finely carved travertine. Mummification took at least 70 days—40 to dry the enormous repository of flesh, and 30 to wrap it.

On the bull's burial day, city residents surged

A. R. Williams is a senior writer for the magazine. Richard Barnes's recent book, Animal Logic, *offers a behind-the-scenes look at natural history museums.*

Ever so gently, archaeologist Salima Ikram flicks at caked mud to free an ibis from the earthenware jar it was buried in 2,700 years ago at Abydos. Back then, millions of stilt-legged ibises bobbed for food in the fertile marshes of the Nile. Symbols of the god Thoth, the birds were mummified in greater numbers than any of the other animals interred at revered sites throughout Egypt (map, opposite).

into the streets to observe this occasion of national mourning. Wailing and tearing at their hair, they crowded the route to the catacomb now known as the Serapeum in the desert necropolis of Saqqara. In procession, priests, temple singers, and exalted officials delivered the mummy to the network of vaulted galleries carved into the bedrock of limestone. There, among the long corridors of previous burials, they interred the mummy in a massive wooden or granite sarcophagus. In later centuries, though, the sanctity of this place was violated as thieves pried off the sarcophagus lids and ransacked the mummies to find their precious ornaments. Sadly, not a single burial of the Apis bull has survived intact.

Different sacred animals were worshipped at their own cult centers—bulls at Armant and Heliopolis, fish at Esna, rams at Elephantine Island, crocodiles at Kom Ombo. Ikram believes the idea of such divine creatures was born at the dawn of Egyptian civilization, a time when heavier rainfall than today made the land green and bountiful. Surrounded by animals, people began to connect them with specific gods according to their habits.

Take crocodiles. They instinctively laid their eggs above the impending high-water line of the Nile's annual flood, the pivotal event that watered and enriched fields and allowed Egypt to be born again year after year. "Crocodiles were magical," Ikram says, "because they had that ability to foretell."

The news of a good flood, or a bad one, was important to a land of farmers. And so, in time, crocodiles became symbols of Sobek, a water god of fertility, and a temple arose at Kom Ombo, one of the places in southern Egypt where the swelling flood was first observed every year. In that sacred space, near the riverbank where wild crocodiles lay sunning themselves, captive crocodiles led an indulged life and were buried with due ceremony after death.

THE MOST NUMEROUS mummies, buried by the millions as at Istabl Antar, were votive objects offered up during yearly festivals at the temples of animal cults. Like county fairs, these great gatherings enlivened religious centers up and down the Nile. Pilgrims arrived by the hundreds of thousands and set up camp. Music and dancing filled the processional route. Merchants sold food, drink, and souvenirs. Priests became salesmen, offering simply wrapped mummies as well as more elaborate ones for people who could spend more—or thought they should. With incense swirling all around, the faithful ended their journey by delivering their chosen mummy to the temple with a prayer.

Some places were associated with just one god and its symbolic animal, but old, venerated sites such as Abydos have yielded whole menageries of votive mummies, each species a link to a particular god. At Abydos, the burial ground of Egypt's first rulers, excavations have uncovered ibis mummies likely representing Thoth, the god of wisdom and writing. Falcons probably evoked the sky-god Horus, protector of the living king. And dogs had ties to the jackal-headed Anubis, the guardian of the dead. By donating one of these mummies to the temple, a pilgrim could win favor with its god. "The creature was always whispering in the god's ear, saying, 'Here he is, here comes your devotee, be nice,'" explains Ikram.

Beginning in the 26th dynasty, in about 664 B.C., votive mummies became wildly popular. The country had just ousted its foreign rulers, and Egyptians were relieved to return to their own traditions. The mummy business boomed, employing legions of specialized workers. Animals had to be bred, cared for, dispatched, and mummified. Resins had to be imported, wrappings prepared, tombs dug.

Despite the lofty purpose of the product, corruption crept into the assembly line, and the occasional pilgrim ended up with something dodgy. "A fakery, a jiggery-pokery," Ikram says. Her x-rays have revealed a variety of ancient consumer rip-offs: a cheaper animal substituted for a rarer, more expensive one; bones or feathers in place of a whole animal; beautiful wrappings around nothing but mud. The more attractive the package, Ikram has discovered, the greater the chance of a scam.

To find out how the ancient embalmers worked—a subject on which the ancient texts are silent or ambiguous—Ikram conducts experiments in mummification. For supplies she visits the labyrinth of Cairo's 14th-century suq. At a small shop just a block from the busy

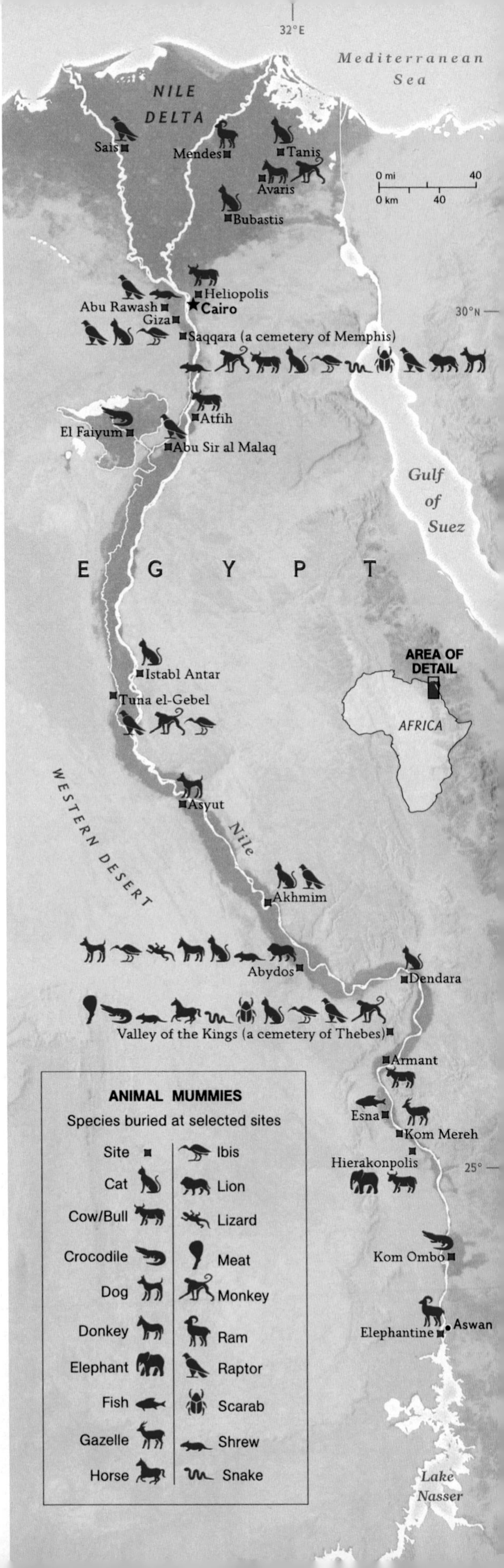

JENNY WANG AND CAITLIN SARGENT; NGM MAPS
SOURCE: NICHOLAS WARNER

ANIMAL MUMMIES

Species buried at selected sites

Site, Cat, Cow/Bull, Crocodile, Dog, Donkey, Elephant, Fish, Gazelle, Horse, Ibis, Lion, Lizard, Meat, Monkey, Ram, Raptor, Scarab, Shrew, Snake

The embalming house for the Apis bulls, sacred animals in the great city of Memphis, survives in ruins near the village of Mit Rahina. For 40 days the body of each bull lay in natron on a massive stone bed in a courtyard where the sun could help desiccate and disinfect it.

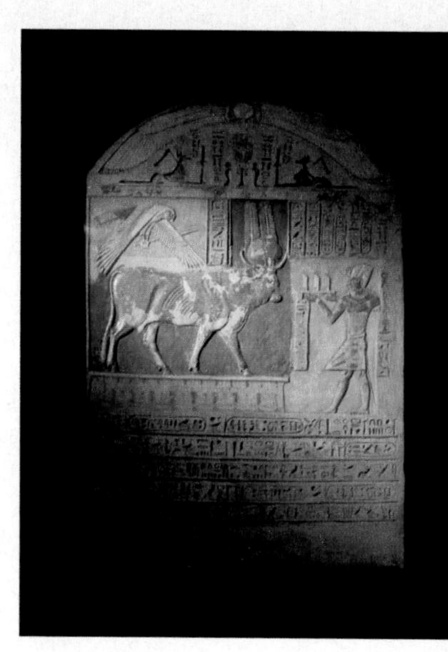

Dedicated upon the death of the sacred Buchis bull at Armant, a stone monument depicts Pharaoh Ptolemy V making an offering to the deceased. Like the bulls of Memphis and Heliopolis, the Buchis was mummified and buried with great ceremony. The holiness of all three bulls extended to their mothers, which were prepared for the next world like this intricately wrapped cow (opposite).

souvenir stands, a clerk uses an old brass balance scale to weigh out kilos of gray crystalline chunks. This is natron, a salt that absorbs moisture and fat and was the key drying agent used in mummification. It's still mined just southwest of the Nile Delta and is usually sold as a washing soda. At the herbalist around the corner, Ikram finds oils that will make dry, stiff bodies flexible again and resinous lumps of frankincense that will seal bandages when melted. No one sells the palm wine that ancient embalmers used to wash out internal cavities after evisceration, so Ikram substitutes locally made gin.

Her mummifications began with rabbits. They're a manageable size, and she could get them at the butcher. "Instead of making them stew bunnies, I gave them life for eternity," she says. Flopsy—Ikram names all her mummies—was buried whole in natron. The body didn't last two days. Gases built up, and it exploded. Thumper had better luck. His lungs, liver, stomach, and intestines were snipped out. He was then stuffed with natron and buried in more of the same. He survived.

Fluffy, the next candidate, helped explain an archaeological puzzle. The natron packed inside her absorbed so much fluid that it became goopy, smelly, and disgusting. Ikram dug out the mess and replaced it with fresh natron tied in linen bags. These were simple to remove once they got soggy, explaining why similar bundles turn up in many embalming caches.

Peter Cottontail's treatment was entirely different. Instead of evisceration, he got a turpentine and cedar-oil enema before being placed in natron. Herodotus, the famed Greek historian, wrote about the procedure in the fifth century B.C., but scholars debate his reliability. In this case, the experiment proved him right. All Peter's innards dissolved except the heart—the one organ ancient Egyptians always left in place.

Like the animals mummified more than 3,000 years ago, Ikram's went to a happy afterlife. Once the lab work was done, she and her students followed protocol and wrapped each body in bandages printed with magical spells. Reciting prayers and burning incense, they laid the mummies to rest in a classroom cabinet, where they draw visitors—including me. As an offering, I sketch plump carrots and symbols to multiply the bunch by a thousand. Ikram assures me that the pictures have instantly become real in the hereafter, and her rabbits are twitching their noses with joy. □

EGYPTIAN MUSEUM (ABOVE); AGRICULTURE MUSEUM

Once swaddled as mummies, the remains
of a dog and two bulls are displayed at

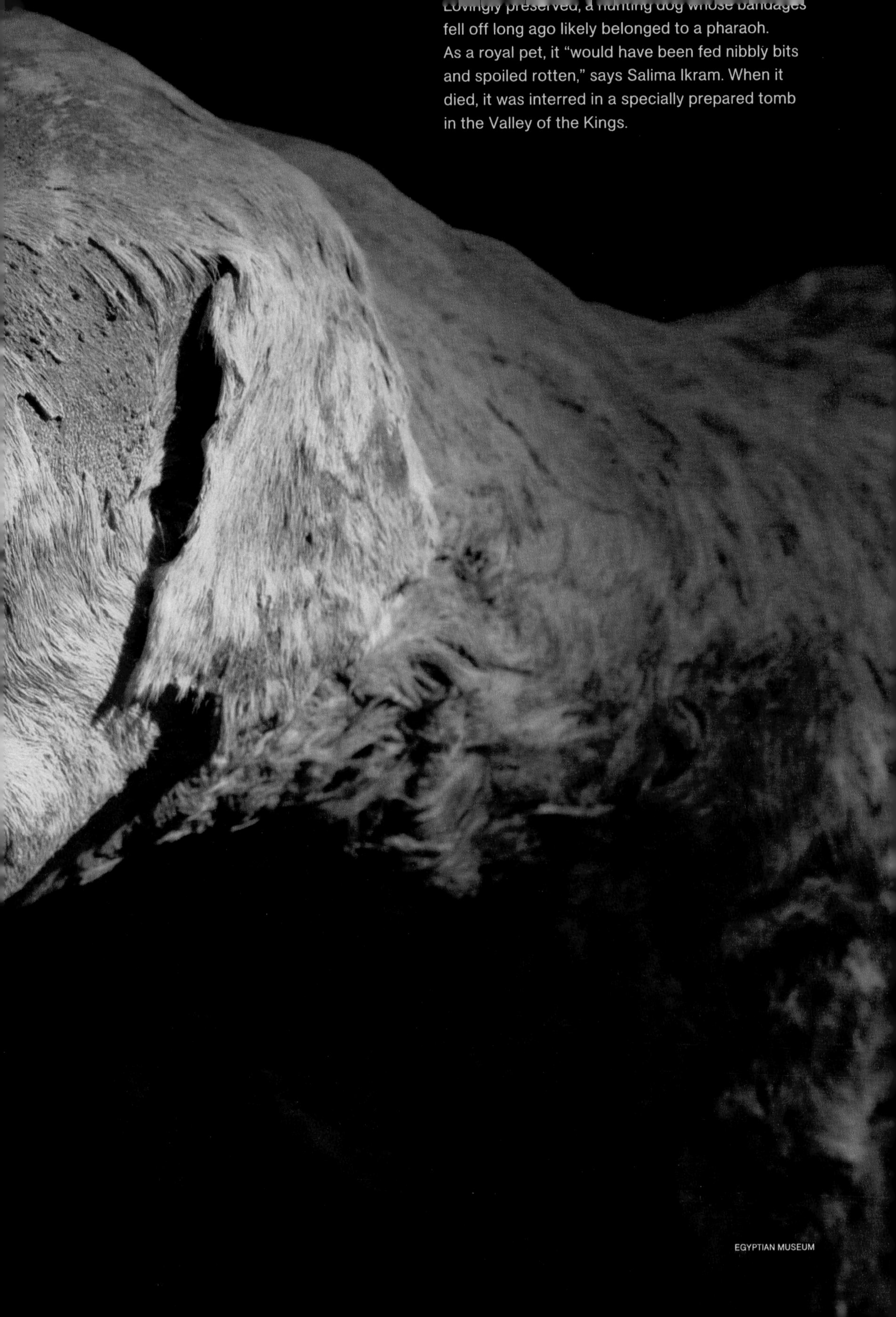

Lovingly preserved, a hunting dog whose bandages fell off long ago likely belonged to a pharaoh. As a royal pet, it "would have been fed nibbly bits and spoiled rotten," says Salima Ikram. When it died, it was interred in a specially prepared tomb in the Valley of the Kings.

EGYPTIAN MUSEUM

Buried with the dog on the preceding pages, a baboon (opposite) harbors a secret that helps identify it as a pet: An x-ray revealed missing canine teeth, probably removed to keep the creature from nipping royal fingers. During mass baboon burials at Tuna el-Gebel (above), priests placed a votive animal in each niche. Thousands of such mummies have been found at the site, and many more likely lie in areas yet to be explored.

EGYPTIAN MUSEUM (LEFT)

SHADOWLAND | POISED TO PLAY A PIVOTAL NEW ROLE IN THE

By Don Belt *Photographs by Ed Kashi*

DAMASCUS VIEWED FROM ATOP MOUNT QASIYUN DURING A CELEBRATION TO MARK THE END OF RAMADAN.

MIDDLE EAST, SYRIA STRUGGLES TO ESCAPE ITS DARK PAST.

Now a tourist attraction, Aleppo's hilltop Citadel has seen a dozen empires rise and fall. Beginning in the 1950s, the government made plans to bulldoze the adjacent Old City, which has straddled

crossroads of trade for 4,500 years. A band of civic officials, architects, and benefactors fought back and finally, decades later, prevailed: In 1986, UNESCO named Aleppo a World Heritage site.

Clamoring for lost lands, Syrians mark Independence Day, April 17, with a visit to the border of the Golan Heights, territory captured by Israel in the Six Day War of 1967. The crowd uses bullhorns to

shout patriotic slogans—and exchange gossip—across the demilitarized zone to the Golan village of Majdal Shams, whose residents remain Syrian citizens despite living on Israeli-occupied land.

THERE'S A PASSAGE in *The Godfather* in which a young Michael Corleone, living abroad, realizes that with his older brother suddenly and violently deceased, he now stands anointed—doomed is more like it—to take over the Mafia empire his aging father has built from scratch. "Tell my father to get me home," he says to his host, resigned to the role he is now fated to play. "Tell my father I wish to be his son."

If there was a moment like that for Bashar al Assad, the current president of Syria, it came sometime after 7 a.m. on January 21, 1994, when the phone rang in his rented apartment in London. A tall, scholarly ophthalmologist, Bashar, then 28, was doing a residency at Western Eye Hospital, part of St. Mary's Hospital system in Britain. Answering the phone, he learned that his older brother, Basil, while racing to the Damascus airport in heavy fog that morning, had driven his Mercedes at high speed through a roundabout. Basil, a dashing and charismatic figure who'd been groomed to succeed their father as president, died instantly in the crash. And now he, Bashar, was being called home.

Fast-forward to June 2000 and the death of the father, Hafez al Assad, of heart failure at age 69. Shortly after the funeral, Bashar entered his father's office for only the second time in his life. He has a vivid memory of his first visit, at age seven, running excitedly to tell his father about his first French lesson. Bashar remembers seeing a big bottle of cologne on a cabinet next to his father's desk. He was amazed to find it still there 27 years later, practically untouched. That detail, the stale cologne, said a lot about Syria's closed and stagnant government, an old-fashioned dictatorship that Bashar, trained in healing the human eye, felt ill-equipped to lead.

"My father never talked to me about politics," Bashar told me. "He was a very warm and caring father, but even after I came home in 1994, everything I learned about his decision-making came from reading the notes he made during meetings, or by talking to his colleagues." One of those lessons was that, unlike performing eye surgery, running a country like Syria requires a certain comfort with ambiguity. Bashar, an avid photographer, compares it with a black-and-white photograph. "There's never pure black or pure white, all bad or all good," he said. "There are only shades of gray."

Syria is an ancient place, shaped by thousands of years of trade and human migration. But if every nation is a photograph, a thousand shades of gray, then Syria, for all its antiquity, is actually a picture developing slowly before our eyes. It's the kind of place where you can sit in a crowded Damascus café listening to a 75-year-old storyteller in a fez conjure up the Crusades and the Ottoman Empire as if they were childhood memories, waving his sword around so wildly that the audience dives for cover—then stroll next door to the magnificent Omayyad Mosque, circa A.D. 715, and join street kids playing soccer on its doorstep, oblivious to the crowds of Iranian pilgrims pouring in for evening prayers or the families wandering by with ice cream. It's also a place where you can dine out with friends at a trendy café, and then, while waiting for a night bus, hear blood-chilling screams coming from a second-floor window of the Bab Touma police station. In the street, Syrians cast each other knowing glances, but no one says a word. Someone might be listening.

The Assad regime hasn't stayed in power for nearly 40 years by playing nice. It has survived a tough neighborhood—bordered by Iraq, Israel, Jordan, Lebanon, and Turkey—by a combination of guile and cozying up to more powerful countries, first the Soviet Union and now Iran. In a state of war with Israel since 1948, Syria provides material support to the Islamist groups of Hezbollah and Hamas; it's also determined

"Dr. Bashar," a U.K.-trained ophthalmologist, became president after the death of his father, Hafez al Assad, who ruled as a dictator for 30 years. Bashar al Assad inherited his father's iron fist, but he also has an eye for reform.

to reclaim the Golan Heights, a Syrian plateau captured by Israel in 1967. Relations with the United States, rarely good, turned particularly dire after the 2003 U.S. invasion of Iraq, when George W. Bush, citing Syria's opposition to the war and support for Iraqi insurgents, threatened regime change in Damascus and demonized Syria's young president as a Middle Eastern prince of darkness.

It's been nearly a decade since Bashar took office, and it's fair to ask what, if anything, has changed. It's also a good time to take stock, as Syria—responding to overtures from a new U.S. administration hungry for success in the Middle East—seems poised to resume a pivotal role in regional affairs. Henry Kissinger famously said you can't make war without Egypt or peace without Syria, and he's probably right. Like it or not, the road to Middle East peace runs right through Damascus. Yet even Bashar acknowledges that it will be hard for Syria to move forward without tending to its crippling internal disrepair.

Outside the ancient Hamadiya market in Damascus, a photograph of Hafez al Assad as tall as a three-story building once stood. Marked by a high forehead and poker player's eyes, the president's giant head peered out over his traffic-choked capital of four million people, as it did from billboards and posters all over Syria. Modeled on the totalitarian cults of the Soviet imperium, this Big Brother iconography always gave Syria the feel of being sealed in amber, trapped in an era when dictators were really dictators, the days of Stalin and Mao. This is the Syria that Hafez left behind.

In its place today, flanked by the city's

Don Belt is the magazine's senior editor for foreign affairs. He and photographer Ed Kashi reported on the plight of Arab Christians in the June 2009 issue.

IT WILL TAKE MORE THAN A SMILE AND A SLOGAN TO REINVENT HIS COUNTRY, AND BASHAR KNOWS IT.

Roman-era walls, is a large white billboard with a photograph of Syria's first postmodern president, waving. Bashar is shown with a buoyant grin on his catlike face, squinting over his whiskers into a bright sun. "I believe in Syria," the billboard says reassuringly. But it will take more than a smile and a slogan to reinvent his country, and he knows it. "What Syria needs now," Bashar told me, "is a change in the mentality."

THE HOME VILLAGE of the Assad family, Al Qardahah, sits on a mountainside facing west, sheltered and aloof as hill towns often are, yet so close to the Mediterranean that on a clear day you can see the fishing boats of Latakia, Syria's largest port, and the seabirds circling like confetti in the western sky. A modern, four-lane expressway rises like a ramp from the coast and delivers supplicants to the remote mountain village, where the streets are paved, houses upscale, and off-duty regime officials—large men in their 50s and 60s who carry themselves like Mafia dons on vacation—pad around town in their pajamas.

Hundreds of years ago Al Qardahah was an enclave of destitute Shiites who followed the Prophet's son-in-law and successor, Ali, so fervently that centuries before they'd been declared heretics by other Muslims and driven into the mountains of northwest Syria, where they came to be known as Alawis. Then in 1939, one of their own—a whip-smart, nine-year-old boy named Hafez—was sent down the mountain to get an education. He lived in Latakia while attending schools run by the French, who had taken over this part of the Ottoman Empire after World War I, in the great carving up of historic Syria (which included present-day Israel, Palestinian territories, Jordan, Lebanon, western Iraq, and southern Turkey) that Britain and France had plotted in the Sykes-Picot Agreement of 1916.

Quiet and tall for his age, Hafez was driven to succeed and ultimately to rule. After Syria gained its independence from France in 1946, he joined the Baath Party, a secular Arab nationalist movement that would seize control of Syria in 1963. Hafez rose through the ranks of the air force and was eventually appointed defense minister. From that position, in 1970, he mounted a bloodless coup with a trusted coterie of military officers, many of them fellow Alawis. Since then, followers of this tiny Shiite sect have managed to hang on to power in this complex, ethnically volatile nation of 20 million people, 76 percent of whom are Sunni—a scenario that one diplomat likens to the Beverly Hillbillies taking charge of California.

Hafez al Assad survived by becoming a world-class manipulator of geopolitical events, playing the weak hand he was dealt so cleverly that Bill Clinton called him the smartest Middle Eastern leader he'd ever met. Inside Syria, Hafez was a master at downplaying the country's potentially explosive religious identities and building an adamantly secular regime. He discouraged the use of the term Alawi in public and changed the name of his home region to the Western mountains; it is still considered impolite to ask about a Syrian's religion today. He also went out of his way to protect other religious minorities—Christians, Ismailis, Druze—because he needed them as a counterweight to the Sunnis.

Hafez was ruthless toward his enemies, especially the Syrian Muslim Brotherhood, a Sunni Islamist movement eager to remove the apostate Alawis from power and make Syria an Islamic state. To counter them, he built an elaborate internal security apparatus modeled after the communist police states of Eastern Europe. When the Brotherhood launched a series of attacks in the late 1970s and early 1980s, Hafez sent his air force to bomb densely populated neighborhoods in the group's stronghold in Hama. His army

MINORITY RULE

Though the population is mostly Sunni Muslim, Syria's ruling family are members of the Alawi sect. An influx of Palestinian and Iraqi refugees—a mix of Christians and Muslims—has added 1.5 million more people to a country of 20 million.

Religions
(percent of Syria's population)

- Sunni Muslim (76%)
- Alawi Muslim (12%)
- Druze Muslim (3%)
- Christian (7%)
- Shiite Muslim, Ismaili Muslim, Yezidi (2%)
- Sparsely populated or uninhabited

Ethnic groups

Arab 90%
Kurd 9%
Armenian and other 1%

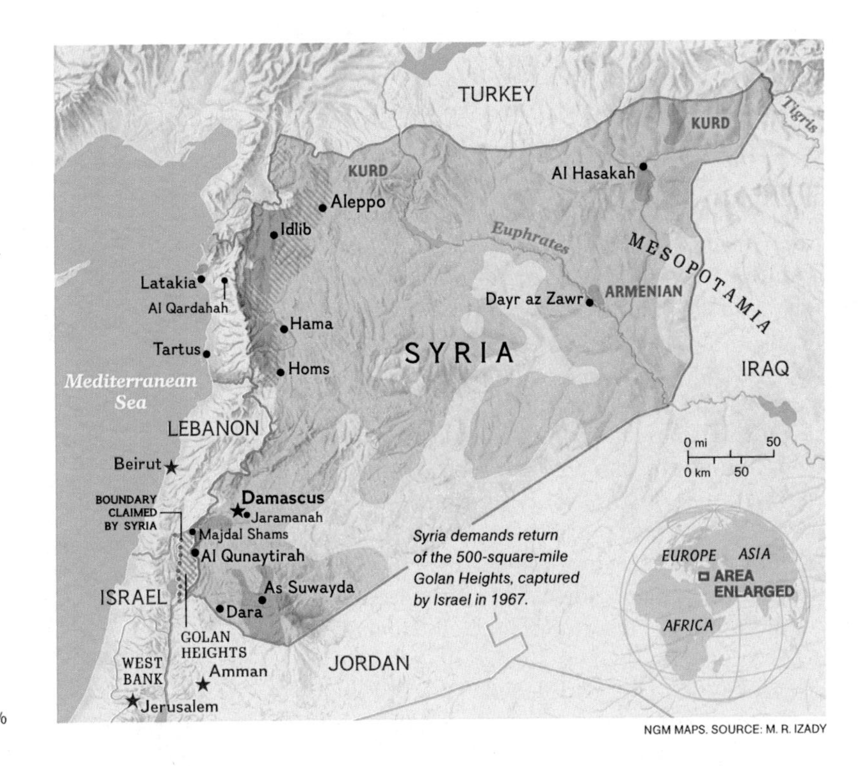

NGM MAPS. SOURCE: M. R. IZADY

bulldozed the smoking remains. Between 10,000 and 40,000 people were killed, and thousands more were jailed, tortured, and left to languish in prison. Despite criticism from human rights organizations, the regime soon unleashed its internal police on all political opponents.

When Hafez al Assad died in 2000, his body was returned to Al Qardahah and placed near that of his firstborn son, Basil, whose adrenaline-charged exploits on horseback, in uniform, and behind the wheel set him apart from his studious younger brother, a soft-spoken health nut whose musical taste runs to Yanni and the Electric Light Orchestra. Yet any suggestion that Bashar is a pushover is an illusion, says Ryan Crocker, who served as U.S. Ambassador in Damascus during the transition from father to son. "Bashar is so personable that it's easy to underestimate him," Crocker says. "But rest assured: He is his father's son."

A YOUNG MAN in an imitation black leather jacket was drawing in my notebook, launching a sailboat on a choppy sea with careful strokes of a blue pen. We were at a café overlooking the stony hills of northern Syria, watching cloud shadows play across a landscape of red soil and silver-green olive trees. Freedom, the man was saying. That's what we need.

"I'm not talking about political freedom," he said, glancing over his shoulder to be sure there were no *mukhabarat,* or secret police, about. "I mean the freedom to do things," he went on, "without getting strangled in rope by bureaucrats. In Syria, for guys like me, there's no incentive to try anything new, to create something. No way. You could never get approval from the government, or even the permits to think about it. Here it all comes down to who you know, what clan or village you're from, how much Vitamin Wow is in your pocket."

"Vitamin Wow?" I said, recalling that there is an Arabic letter pronounced "wow."

"*Wasta!*" he said, laughing. Money! Bribes!

"Where is your sailboat going?" I asked, nodding at his sketch.

"Nowhere," he said, grinning. "I've got no Vitamin Wow!"

Shortly after Bashar returned from London, he diagnosed Syria as suffering from an overdose of Vitamin Wow. After taking office in 2000, he launched a tough anticorruption campaign, firing a number of ministers and bureaucrats and vowing to replace old, wasta-loving ways with the "new mentality" he was seeking to instill. Swept up in the spirit of reform, he went on to release hundreds of political prisoners and eased the restrictions on political dissent—a so-called Damascus Spring that quickly spread from living rooms to a growing subculture of Internet cafés. It was Bashar himself who had made this last trend possible, working with like-minded technocrats to computerize Syria even before he became president. Over the objections of the country's powerful military-intelligence complex, Bashar had persuaded his father to connect Syria to the World Wide Web in 1998.

He also took steps to reboot Syria's stagnant economy. "Forty years of socialism—this is what we're up against," said Abdallah Dardari, 46, a London-educated economist who serves as deputy prime minister for economic affairs. Bashar has recruited Syria's best and brightest expatriates to return home. The new team has privatized the banking system, created duty-free industrial parks, and opened a Damascus stock exchange to encourage more of the private and foreign investment that has quickened the pulse of the capital and launched dozens of upscale nightclubs and restaurants.

"My job is to deliver for the people of Syria," said Bashar, who is known for occasionally dropping by a restaurant, leaving the bodyguards outside, to share a meal with other diners. In his push to modernize, Bashar's most potent ally is his wife, the former Asma al-Akhras, a stylish, Western-educated business executive who has launched a number of government-sponsored programs for literacy and economic empowerment. Daughter of a prominent Syrian heart specialist, Asma was born and raised in London. She and Bashar have three children, whom they're fond of taking on picnics and bicycle

Enrollment at Al Sit school for girls in Damascus has doubled with the influx of some 1.4 million Iraqi refugees. Though welcoming, Syrian schools are busy with struggles of their own: modernizing teaching techniques and textbooks.

A street scene in Damascus's Old City (photographed from inside a shop selling mirrors) reflects the diversity of modern Syria, where head scarves mix with jeans and trendy accessories. Bashar al Assad led

a group of young technocrats who connected Syrians to the Internet in 1998, yet as president he has cracked down on Web use. His country skews young, with more than half the population under age 24.

Drilling on pain-free plastic, dental students attend Kalamoun, Syria's first private university, built to compete with public schools where training is reserved for champion test-takers and the politically connected. Syria's stock exchange (bottom) opened this past March, another step toward privatization.

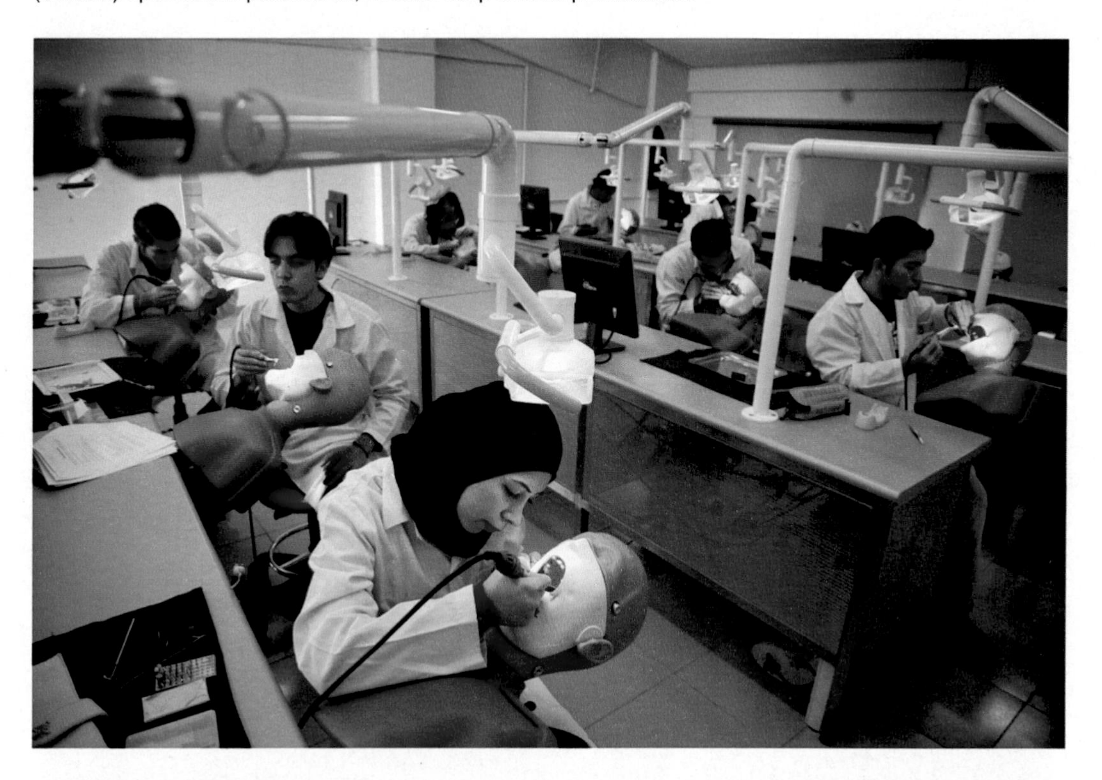

rides in the hills around the capital—a marked contrast to Hafez al Assad, who was rarely seen in public. "You only know what people need if you come in contact with them," Bashar said. "We refuse to live inside a bubble. I think that's why people trust us."

WHEN I ASKED IF THE FACTORY MADE A PROFIT, HE LOOKED AT ME AS IF I WERE SPEAKING IN TONGUES.

FOR MORE THAN 4,000 YEARS, the city of Aleppo in northern Syria has been a crossroads for trade moving along the Fertile Crescent from Mesopotamia to the Mediterranean. Guarded by a towering hilltop Citadel, Aleppo's 900-acre Old City has remained essentially intact since the Middle Ages. Today, entering its covered suq, the largest in the Arab world, is like stepping across some cobblestone threshold into the 15th century—a medieval mosh pit of shopkeepers, food vendors, gold merchants, donkey carts, craftsmen, trinket peddlers, beggars, and hustlers of all stripes, moving in a great colorful clanking parade of goat bells and sandaled feet. If Aleppo bureaucrats had gotten their way, much of this would be gone.

During the 1950s, urban planners in Aleppo began implementing a modern development plan, dissecting the Old City with wide, Western-style streets. In 1977, local residents, led by an Old City architect named Adli Qudsi, fought back and eventually got the government to change its plan. Today the Old City has been preserved and its infrastructure overhauled, with funds from both government and philanthropic sources. Once considered a crumbling relic, old Aleppo is now cited by Bashar as a prime example of the new mentality he's seeking, a model for how Syria's past, its greatest asset, can be retooled and made into a future.

"Syria has been a trading nation for millennia, so what we're trying to do is return the country to its entrepreneurial roots," said Dardari. "But it's not going to be easy: 25 percent of the Syrian workforce still draws a government paycheck. We've inherited an economy that runs on patronage and government money, and we can't keep it up."

To see what Dardari and the modernizers are up against, I toured a government cotton-processing plant in Aleppo reminiscent of factories in the Soviet Union, vast and crumbling monuments to rusty machinery. The plant manager rambled on like a good apparatchik about the aging factory's production figures and impeccable safety record—unaware that a group of workers had just told me about the lost fingers, crushed feet, and lung damage they had suffered. When I asked if the factory made a profit, he looked at me as if I were speaking in tongues.

By allowing private investment in state-run industries, starting with cement and oil processing, Bashar and his reformers hope to modernize their operations and run them more efficiently. Many jobs have been lost in the process, and prices, no longer subsidized, have soared. But so many Syrians depend on government-supplied incomes from the cotton industry—a primary source of export revenue—that it remains mostly state run.

In many respects, the Syria that Bashar inherited bears all the signs of an antique enterprise, ready for the wrecking ball. Built by the Syrian Baath Party in the 1960s, the system of state enterprises and government jobs raised living standards and brought education and health care to rural villages, but its foundation resembles the corrupt and moribund Eastern-bloc socialism that collapsed under its own weight in the early 1990s. The Syrian bureaucracy is even older, having been erected from the fallen timbers of Ottoman and French colonial rule.

Education reform is also on Bashar's drawing board, and not a moment too soon. Syrian schoolchildren are taught by rote memorization from aging textbooks, and judged, even at the university level, by the number of facts they know. In Damascus, once revered as an intellectual

Barefoot farmers in the fields near Idlib stomp 300 pounds of cotton into each burlap bag, which is then muscled onto a truck and hauled to collection centers. Most cotton—a primary export and a vital

source of jobs—is grown on private farms but ginned at public mills, a remnant of the state-run industries that once dominated Syria's economy, modeled on the socialism of the Soviet bloc.

LIVING IN SYRIA IS LIKE WALKING SIDEWAYS WITH A LADDER, HAVING TO WATCH EVERY MOVE YOU MAKE.

capital of the eastern world, it's hard to find a bookstore that isn't stocked with communist-era treatises penned by Baath Party ideologues.

"My 11-year-old daughter is so confused," said Dardari. "She hears from me at home about free markets and the way the world works, and then she goes to school and learns from textbooks written in the 1970s that preach Marxism and the triumph of the proletariat. She comes home with this look on her face and says, 'Daddy, I feel like a Ping-Pong ball!'"

WHEN A SON GOES into the family business, the old way of doing things can be very hard to change. And even though the eldest son, Basil, was considered more like his father, Bashar has ended up following in his footsteps—in more ways than one. A year into his presidency, planes hit the World Trade Center in New York City, and suddenly the threat to secular, "non-Muslim" regimes like Syria's from al Qaeda and its cousins in the Muslim Brotherhood appeared stronger than ever. The U.S. invasion of Iraq—and subsequent saber rattling toward Damascus—inflamed Syria's Islamists even further, while swamping the country with some 1.4 million Iraqi refugees, most of whom never returned home. Some believe that Bashar, in a move reminiscent of his father, diverted the widespread rage in Syria away from his vulnerable regime toward the Americans across the border in Iraq, allowing jihadists to use Syria as a staging area and transit point.

Even before 9/11, Bashar had backtracked on political reform and freedom of expression. His anticorruption drive had stalled, undermined by the shady business dealings of his own extended family. Investigations into the 2005 assassination of former Lebanese Prime Minister Rafiq Hariri in Beirut led to Syria's doorstep; shortly thereafter Bashar rearrested many of the political prisoners he'd released just a few years earlier. And last year, in an ironic twist for a self-confessed computer nerd who brought the Internet to Syria, Bashar's government banned a long list of websites, ranging from Arabic news sites to YouTube and Facebook. In all this, some see Bashar as the victim of reactionary elements within the regime—the youthful idealist dragged down by forces he is powerless to resist. Others see a young godfather learning to flex his muscles.

Bashar blames the U.S. invasion of Iraq for pushing the region, and Syria, into a dark corner and defends his tough internal security measures as vital weapons in the struggle to survive. Whether he's talking about the survival of Syria, or his regime, is unclear. "We're in a state of war with Israel," he said. "We've had conflicts with the Muslim Brotherhood since the 1950s. But now we have a much worse danger from al Qaeda. Al Qaeda is a state of mind. It's a CD, it's a booklet. And it's very hard to detect. This is why we need a strong internal security."

Members of the opposition, nearly all of them underground or in jail, don't buy that argument, having heard it used for 30 years to smother any spark of dissent. While acknowledging that today's repression is administered with a lighter touch, the activists I talked to consider the differences between Bashar's regime and his father's to be cosmetic. "Bashar seems like a pretty nice guy, but the government is more than one person," said a young human rights activist I met secretly with in a tiny, book-lined apartment on the outskirts of the capital. He'd been interrogated a half dozen times by various agencies of state security. "Living here is something like a phobia," he went on, smoking a cigarette, dark circles under his eyes. "You always feel like someone's watching. You look around and there's no one there. So you think, I shouldn't have this feeling, but I do. I must be crazy. This is what they want."

Whatever its purpose, Syria's shadow of fear, the cloud that blocks its sun, is pervasive. To

Feted for her first Communion, Marla Baqleh of Jaramanah immortalizes a tableful of pastries. Christians and other religious minorities are vigorously protected by the Assad regime, itself drawn from a tiny Shiite sect. In a nearby hammam, fathers and sons enjoy the intimate ancient rituals of the baths.

In varied states of devotion, pilgrims worship at the Sayida Zainab shrine in Damascus. This is the traditional resting place of Zainab, granddaughter of the Prophet Muhammad and daughter of Ali, Islam's

fourth caliph, who is revered by Shiites. In crowded neighborhoods around the mosque, tens of thousands of Iraqi refugees mingle with visitors from Iran, who make up a sizable portion of Syria's tourists.

School's out in the Western mountains, home to the Alawi clans—and the ruling family of Syria. Their trademark: the watchful gaze of late strongman Hafez al Assad (background, at center), his image flanked by portraits of his sons.

protect my sources for this article, I've left a number of people unnamed, fearing that they'd be arrested once it's published. An academician I met in Aleppo, for example, was harshly interrogated after attending a conference where Israeli scientists were present. After trying to browbeat him into informing on others, the interrogators let him go with a warning not to breathe a word or his file would be reopened. In Idlib, an Islamic fundamentalist hotbed south of Aleppo, a merchant compared living in Syria, with its internal security apparatus, to "walking sideways with a ladder, always having to think ahead and watch every little move you make."

ONE MORNING in Damascus, I was talking to a group of day laborers in a park, scruffy guys in their late teens and early twenties who were looking for work. Most were from southern Syria around Dara, and we were debating what kind of city Dara is. They were bad-mouthing it as a dry and dirty hellhole; I was defending it, having passed through a number of times on my way to Jordan. While we were bantering, a bullish, middle-aged man in a green polo shirt and wraparound sunglasses drifted over and listened in. As the workers became aware of him, our discussion murmured to a halt.

"Dara is a truly great city," the newcomer finally said, with an air of steely finality. The others moved away, suddenly afraid of this man. To see what he would do, I told him I was scheduled to see the president and asked if he'd like me to convey a message. He stared at me for a long moment, then went over and sat on a bench, scribbling in a notebook. I figured he was writing a report on me, or perhaps issuing some kind of ticket. A few minutes later, he was back.

"Please pass this to the president," he said, handing me a slip of paper folded so many times it was the size of a spitball. Then he turned and walked away. On it he had scrawled his name and phone number and a message in rough Arabic: "Salute, Dr. President Bashar, the respected. This paper is from a national Syrian young man from Al Hasakah who needs very much a job in the field of public office, and thank you." □

BLAZE OF BLUE

KINGFISHERS

Its perch serving as lookout and diving board, a kingfisher waits above the still waters of an English river, which reflects trees and sky. This flashy hunter can dive and return with a fish in two seconds.

An azure blur, a kingfisher plummets toward the water, reaching speeds of more than 25 miles an hour. The bird's aim is so unerring that even though a protective translucent membrane veils its eyes underwater (right), it can confidently catch fish to depths of two feet.

In a prey's-eye view, an adult female snaps up a stickleback, a small spiny fish, from just beneath the water's surface. Beak color gives away a kingfisher's gender: Males show mostly black, while females have an orange lower mandible that matches their feet.

BY HANNAH HOLMES ▪ PHOTOGRAPHS BY CHARLIE HAMILTON JAMES

A FLASH OF ELECTRIC BLUE—that's as intimately as most people will ever know the common kingfisher. But it suffices. ▪ "Everyone in England who has ever seen one will remember where they saw it," says photographer and kingfisher thrall Charlie Hamilton James. "I saw my first one when I was a boy. I've been completely obsessed ever since." For a few years he traipsed empty-handed after the bird near Bristol, in southwest England. Later, to justify the hours spent on the gloomy riverbanks that kingfishers haunt, he took along a camera. That was 20 years ago.

Alcedo atthis (also known as the Eurasian, European, or river kingfisher) has inspired many an obsession. In the world's temperate zones, where drab plumage is the norm, this kingfisher, unlike its North American cousins, bedazzles. Slicing the air like a turquoise missile, it is impossible to disregard.

The yellow, red, orange, and brown birds of the world assume their hues because of a pigment embedded in the keratin matrix of feathers. But blue feathers result from refraction, a prism-style splitting of light inside a feather. Under a microscope each long kingfisher barb, finer than a human hair, glitters with shades of the Caribbean. Tiny structures in the feathers choreograph incoming light, reflecting sapphire in one direction, emerald in another.

COMMON KINGFISHER RANGE
(Alcedo atthis)

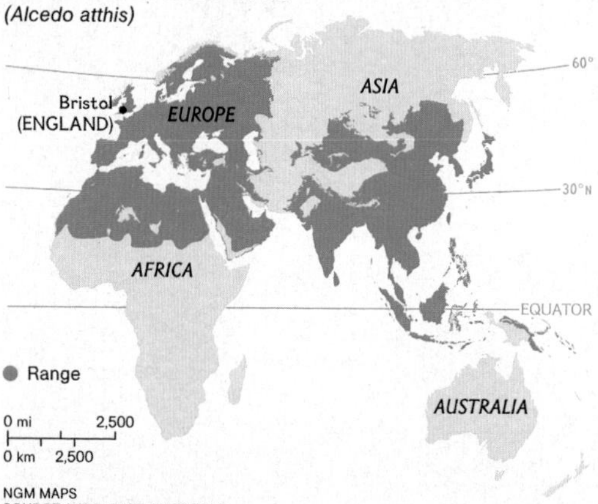

60°
30° N
EQUATOR
Bristol (ENGLAND)
EUROPE
ASIA
AFRICA
AUSTRALIA
● Range
0 mi 2,500
0 km 2,500

NGM MAPS
SOURCE: WORLD WILDLIFE FUND

Alas, beauty can be a curse. At times, kingfisher feathers have achieved the status of gemstones, silk, and spices. A third-century Chinese text describing Western cultures included a list of treasures that might be extracted from the Roman Empire: ivory, gold, carnelian, pearls, kingfisher feathers. Over the course of 2,500 years, the Chinese fashion industry plucked an inconceivable number of birds from the forests of Asia. In an art form called *tian tsui*, or dotting with kingfishers, craftsmen applied the shimmering feathers to jewelry, fans, privacy screens, and landscape panels. Entire quilts were reportedly transformed into blue-green seascapes. Korean royalty shared the passion, which finally faded in the early 1900s.

Fortunately, these days the little spitfire's rarity is an illusion. The kingfisher isn't shy; it simply exploits an environment most people (with the exception of Hamilton James and his sort) avoid. The ideal riverbank is crumbly enough for the birds to excavate a nesting burrow with their beaks. The nest should be sufficiently high to ride out occasional floods and sufficiently low to thwart foxes, snakes, and other raiders trying to penetrate from above.

Solitary most of the year, each individual strives to protect enough real estate to guarantee steady fishing and a good nest site. "These tiny little birds have got to hold down a whole mile of river," explains Hamilton James. Neither male nor female will hesitate in the defense of this life-sustaining territory. At just an ounce and a half, a kingfisher is a force to be reckoned with. "They're very loud, and they tell everyone they're coming," says Hamilton James. "I suppose they are quite arrogant."

In a riverbank burrow a mother feeds one of her nine-day-old chicks a small fish, which it will swallow whole.

Disputes begin with high-speed chases and the occasional beak jab. If aerial jousting doesn't settle the argument, things may turn deadly. At the river's edge two birds will lock beaks and attempt to force each other underwater.

Breeding season requires a pause in the usual hostilities between sexes. The male's opening move is direct: He hurtles after his former foe, whistling urgently. If she tolerates his company, he will ply her with fresh fish, directing them headfirst into her beak. On occasions when a truce is struck between neighbors, the pair will merge territories—temporarily. From their joint holdings they'll either select an old nest for reuse or start anew. Chiseling a two-foot tunnel can take ten days of hard labor for the pair.

After three weeks of brooding, the eggs hatch. Hardly fastidious homemakers, the birds raise their nestlings in the dark on a layer of tiny fish bones regurgitated as pellets, then shattered with a perfunctory peck. (Hamilton James has watched this behavior from a subterranean observatory adjoining a nest.) Both parents fish in earnest. The kingfisher is an ambush hunter, perching over a river until a small fish flicks into range. It can plummet, strike, and wing back to its perch in the space of two blurry seconds. It thumps the catch against the branch to stun it—a lesson some young birds learn only after swallowing a stickleback that erects its dorsal spine on the way down. For the three or four weeks that chicks are in the nest, the adults may bring home 50 to 70 fish a day, and that messy layer of fish bones builds up.

What kingfishers lack in fine manners they make up for in fecundity. Many bird species will raise a second brood, but kingfishers, averaging six or seven eggs per clutch, often raise a third. One pair was observed raising a fourth.

Zealous reproduction helps the species thrive. Throughout its range, the kingfisher's status is stable enough that very few ornithologists pay it much heed. The handful of *Alcedo atthis* scholars report that it is one of the wild animals that don't mind rubbing shoulders with humans—good news in an increasingly urban world.

Hamilton James observes that his local birds are always willing to annex a backyard goldfish pond. And Japanese ornithologist Satoe Kasahara says that lately kingfishers have snatched fish from urban ponds in her country. Across the kingfisher's range, wherever rivers are healthy, fish will swim. And where the fish go, the flashy little bird with the sassy whistle is likely to follow. □

Hannah Holmes's most recent book is The Well-Dressed Ape: A Natural History of Myself. *Charlie Hamilton James is equally compelled by otters and kingfishers.*

"The Kingfisher rises out of the black wave like a blue flower," wrote poet Mary Oliver, paying tribute to the dashing river bird on its feeding rounds. Light scatters prismatically in microscopic feather structures to create the kingfisher's brilliant blue.

Climber John Benson weaves through skin-ripping pinnacles. In Malagasy, the formations are called *tsingy,* meaning "where one cannot walk barefoot." The terrain resists intrusions from hunters, hungry cattle, and wildfires.

BY NEIL SHEA

PHOTOGRAPHS BY STEPHEN ALVAREZ

The lizard moved in frightened rhythms across the sun-blasted stone. A few quick steps, a turn of its boxy head. Then the stillness, the absolute zero, of a creature that sensed it was being hunted. All around, jagged spires and flutes rose like the towers of some Gothic cathedral, silent and empty. From the canyons below, a parrot flew squawking, breaking the trance. The lizard launched. Hery Rakotondravony's arm fired out. Moments later the young herpetologist uncurled his fingers. "I think this is a new species."

In the few days we'd spent in Madagascar's Tsingy de Bemaraha national park and reserve, it was the second or third time he'd said this. On an island famous for its biodiversity (90 percent of the species here are endemic, found nowhere else on Earth), the 600-square-mile protected area is an island unto itself, a kind of biofortress, rugged, largely unexplored, and made nearly impenetrable by the massive limestone formation—the *tsingy*—running through it.

The great block of Jurassic stone has dissolved into a labyrinth of knife-edged towers, slot canyons, and wet caves that ward off humans while harboring other animals and plants. New species are frequently described from the isolated habitats within—a previously unknown coffee plant in 1996, a minuscule lemur in 2000, a bat in 2005, a frog two years later. Even larger animals have been found relatively recently, including a long-legged lemur discovered in 1990 but named, somewhat whimsically, only in 2005 after British comedian and conservation advocate John Cleese.

Steven Goodman, a biologist with the Field Museum in Chicago who has lived and worked in Madagascar for 20 years, describes the region

Contributing Writer Neil Shea's winter adventure on Mount Washington appeared in February. Stephen Alvarez photographed caves for the June issue.

Sunlight rakes the heights of the tsingy, where any rainfall is quickly shed. The arid upper reaches favor mobile creatures such as dragonflies (here in a cooling posture) as well as spiny, drought-tolerant *Pachypodium* plants (above).

as "a refuge within paradise," a place where a kind of biology more familiar a century ago can still be practiced and where simply walking around might put you face-to-face with a creature never seen before.

"You can move between valleys and find different things," Goodman said. "The tsingy formations of Madagascar are one of the places on Earth that hold extraordinary biological treasures. You just have to go in and look around."

Going in is the hard part. In March, at the end of the rainy season, just before the leaves browned and fell and winter dried the forest's thin streams, photographer Stephen Alvarez and I traveled into the park. Rakotondravony had agreed to guide us. It was his fourth trip to the Tsingy de Bemaraha; he is one of a handful of scientists who have gone there more than once.

We arrived in the capital, Antananarivo, just after the president had been overthrown in a coup. Violent protests flared every few days. Near the main square, soldiers lazed in transport trucks smoking and sending text messages, while on the university campus, students rallied beneath white banners, only to be driven back brutally. Tourism, a mainstay of the economy, had nearly collapsed. We left the city wondering if we'd be stopped. But soon, in the countryside, signs of the coup receded, the weight of it felt only at police checkpoints, where men in sandals cradled old AK-47s and asked where we were going.

It took nearly five days to reach the tsingy. Three days out, the route deteriorated into a deeply rutted dirt track that plunged through troughs of dark mud. Ferries carried us across rivers red with soil washed away in the aftermath of deforestation upstream. Villages shrank, cars vanished, the forest gradually thickened. Every few miles Rakotondravony leaped from our truck and ran into the bush. He'd return hauling a large snake or some unhappy lizard.

From a trailhead *(Continued on page 104)*

200 MILLION YEARS AGO

DEPOSITED

A bed of unusually pure limestone more than a thousand feet deep was deposited in a Jurassic lagoon.

UPLIFTED

Tectonic shifts slowly elevated the limestone formation, further exposed as sea levels fell during ice ages.

1.8 MILLION YEARS AGO

DISSOLVING

Caves formed where groundwater dissolved the stone along fracture lines created by the tectonic uplift.

EXPANDING

The fluctuating water table scoured and enlarged the caves. Rain drilled down from the surface.

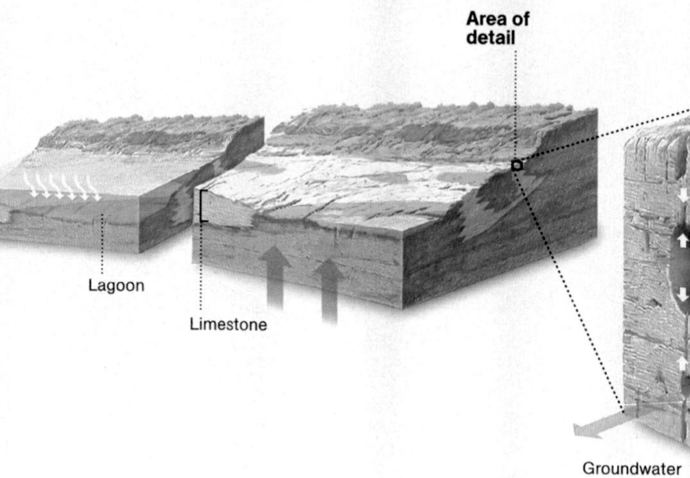

Water table

Fractures

Monsoon rains

Groundwater

Caves merged to form deeper caves

CARVING A JAGGED MAZE

The razor-backed canyons of the Tsingy de Bemaraha formed largely beneath the surface as deep, narrow caves. While monsoon rains chiseled the top of an expansive limestone deposit, subterranean groundwater dissolved the stone along a grid of fracture lines. When cave roofs collapsed and the water table fell, a labyrinth of canyons, called grikes, emerged, creating what geologist Márton Veress calls a "truly outrageous landscape."

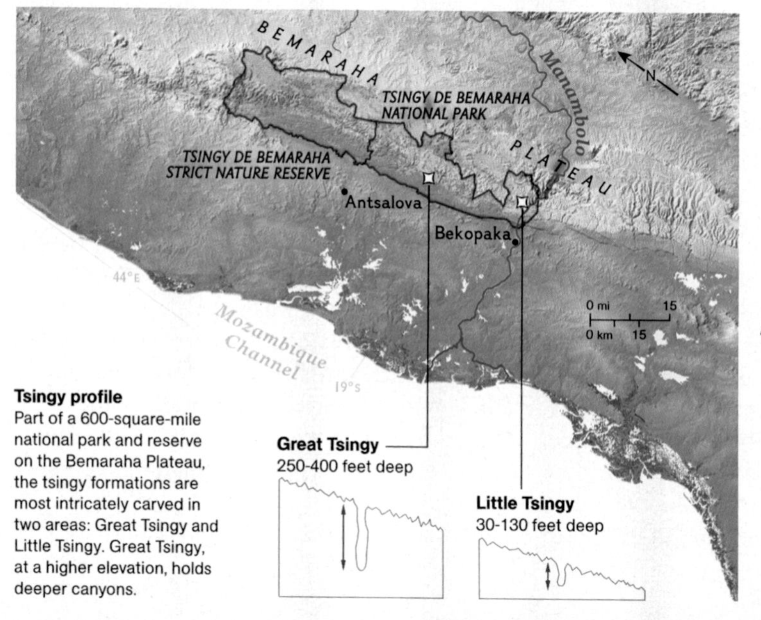

Tsingy profile
Part of a 600-square-mile national park and reserve on the Bemaraha Plateau, the tsingy formations are most intricately carved in two areas: Great Tsingy and Little Tsingy. Great Tsingy, at a higher elevation, holds deeper canyons.

TODAY
OPEN CANYONS
Canyons were revealed as cave ceilings tumbled and the water table fell. Today groundwater still shapes new caves and other features.
Scalloped surfaces of the canyon walls show that they were cut by sediment-laden groundwater rather than rain.
Groundwater
Natural bridge formed by fallen boulder
Pinnacles
Natural bridge
0 feet
10
20
30
40
50
60
70
80
90
100
Rain dissolved the top several feet
Most of the tsingy formed as caves, reaching as deep as 400 feet.
Bottom channel
Notches
Grike
Roundabout cave
Caves are both parallel and perpendicular to one another.
ART BY FERNANDO G. BAPTISTA, NG STAFF; SEAN McNAUGHTON, NG STAFF
SOURCE: MÁRTON VERESS, UNIVERSITY OF WEST HUNGARY
NGM MAPS

Fearless acrobat, a Decken's sifaka leaps a chasm a hundred feet deep to land on a splinter of stone (above). Troops of these primates, found only in western Madagascar, cruise the tops of the tsingy searching for food and evading predators. Like other lemurs, they probably live in small family groups. Little is known about their behavior, but evolution has equipped them with thick pads on hands and feet, helping them navigate their serrated home (preceding pages).

(Continued from page 95) near a small village, we hiked into the forest. After several months of rain, the prolonged dry period was beginning, when many creatures estivate, waiting for the wet to return. We pitched tents near a clear stream, with rust-colored crabs flitting through the shallows. Our kitchen was set beneath an overhang in a cliff that rose through the canopy and, far above, split and cracked into the needles and fins and towers that give the place its name.

IN MALAGASY *TSINGY* MEANS "where one cannot walk barefoot," but we found that the landscape demanded much more than sturdy shoes. In several spots we tried exploring using rock-climbing gear. The tsingy chewed equipment and flesh with equal ease. At times it was like climbing amid giant skewers, the consequences of a fall suggested in the mutilated trunks of toppled trees below. In other places we explored the labyrinth on foot, following faint trails used by locals hunting honey or lemurs.

We squeezed through passages, our pack straps catching on fingers of stone. Finding handholds and footholds required concentration and testing, to see if the rock was too sharp or if it would hold weight. We stemmed narrow ravines and nervously straddled fins that were like fences topped with broken glass. The rock pierced our boots, leaving holes in the rubber. Usually we came over needle-sharp rises only to descend onto mats of thin soil covering yet more serrated rock. We'd carefully find our balance, then try to figure out what to do next.

We were lucky to cover half a mile a day—imagine trying to cross a city by climbing up each high-rise and then down the other side. Our slow progress made us easy targets for mosquitoes and wasps, and it underscored how difficult biological research here must be, dragging equipment and specimens through the terrain. But even covering far less ground than we'd hoped, we saw hundreds of animals and plants, more than we could recognize. In quieter moments it was possible to imagine a thousand places humans had never been, might never go.

One afternoon, returning from a hot, wet slog, vines along the trail tripped me up, and my right knee landed on a small rock. Back home in New England, where rocks come in rounder forms, I would have walked away with a bruise. But this was tsingy in miniature. A barb of limestone drove in nearly to the bone. It took two days to reach a hospital, where a nurse removed dirt from the wound. "Why were you doing this?" she asked, twisting a swab deep into the hole. She looked up. I was sweating. "I think you are a little dumb," she said. The tsingy is the perfect foil to human ambition.

THE UNUSUAL FORMATIONS HERE are a type of karst system, a landscape formed from porous limestone that was dissolved, scoured, and shaped by water. The exact processes that carved such an otherworldly stonescape are complex and rare; only a few similar karst formations exist outside Madagascar. Researchers believe that groundwater infiltrated the great limestone beds and began to dissolve them along joints and faults, creating caves and tunnels. The cavities grew, and eventually their roofs collapsed along the same joints, creating line-straight canyons called grikes, up to 400 feet deep and edged by spires of standing rock. Some grikes are so tight that a human traveler has difficulty passing through them; others are as wide as an avenue.

Observing the tsingy from the air, pilots have been reminded of the deep urban canyons of Manhattan, where an angular, chaotic skyline descends into a grid of streets and alleys, buildings and parks, everything underlain by a circulatory system of pipes, sewers, and train tunnels. The metaphor applies to the tsingy's inhabitants as well, because the formations have become like rows of high-rise apartment buildings, providing shelter to a different array of species at each level.

At the highest reaches there is little soil and no shelter from the sun. Here temperatures often bake above 90°F, and plant and animal life is restricted to creatures that can resist desiccation or move between the pinnacles and the

Vertical pupils identify a *seseke*, or leaf-tailed gecko, as a nocturnal creature. Its camouflage works so well that the lizard doesn't hide during the day. It simply flattens itself against tree trunks while waiting for darkness and insects to eat.

canyons. Lemurs like the white-furred Decken's sifaka and the brown lemur use the tsingy as a kind of highway, leaping from spire to spire as they travel between fruit trees. In slots and crevices lizards chase insects through gardens of drought-tolerant xerophytes—euphorbias, aloes, spine-covered *Pachypodium,* and other plants that drop long, cablelike roots into the rock searching for water.

In the middle ranges of the high-rise, more niches appear in the canyon walls. Large fruit bats and dark vasa parrots roost here, their cackles and cries echoing through vaulted chambers and crumbling galleries. In shadier spots, bees anchor their nests in holes in the stone.

But it is in the humid grike bottoms, where water and soil collect, that the environment is richest. Here, among arrays of orchids and enormous tropical hardwoods, roams a bestiary: giant snails and fist-size, cricket-like insects, large chameleons, emerald green snakes, and red rats. The lemur-eating fossa—a wiry, thin-coated mammal with retractable claws that resembles something like a large cat—also patrols the tsingy. Finally, below the soil and the mud are caves and tunnel passages, the subway system where fish, crabs, insects, and other creatures live and commute, some without ever surfacing.

This walled city has sheltered its residents even as Madagascar's other ecosystems disintegrated. Scientists call it the perfect refuge.

THE CONCEPT OF "REFUGE" in biology signifies a safe zone, like a refugee camp, to which living things withdraw as their habitat shrinks. Once they become cloistered in refuges, animals and plants often become increasingly distinct from even their close relatives. Madagascar itself epitomizes this process, so unusual and removed are many of its species from their cousins on the African continent. Lemurs are the island's best known creatures. Their precursors once inhabited Africa but eventually went extinct there, leaving the continent to other primates,

Often no wider than a hiker's shoulders, slot canyons swallow water in the rainy season, funneling much of it to underground chambers. The passages remain moist year-round, supporting dozens of species of invertebrates and amphibians. Most local people who enter the tsingy seek the sweet prize of honey (below).

and today lemurs are found only in Madagascar. Free from the competition that likely drove them to extinction elsewhere, they evolved into richly varied forms, including now vanished species that were big as gorillas and the palm-size mouse lemur, the smallest living primate.

The tsingy also provides refuge on a smaller scale. Protected by walls of stone and wet by seasonal rains, the forest within is very different from the palm savanna curling around it to the east and the coastal areas that flank it to the west. It is a relict of another era, when forest corridors might have linked one side of the island with the other.

In recent millennia a natural drying trend fractured those corridors. Then came people. Since the first humans arrived in Madagascar some 2,300 years ago, nearly 90 percent of the island's original habitat has been destroyed, most of it harvested for timber or felled or burned to create room for crops and, more recently, cattle. As a result, many of the species that lived on the island are thought to have gone extinct.

In the west the tsingy walls in a large portion of forest. The stone serves as a barrier to human settlement and to cattle, which threaten wildlife habitat all across Africa with their plodding hooves and insatiable appetites. The tsingy also acts as a firebreak, shielding the forest from fires—both natural and those set by humans.

"Bemaraha has unusual animal and plant populations in part because the surrounding area has been changed, either by humans or by climate change," said Brian Fisher, curator of entomology at the California Academy of Sciences. "We've found it's much more diverse than we initially thought."

ONE SWELTERING MORNING Rakotondravony and I hiked into a tangled forest lining the floor of a grike. We paused at a large ant mound, red ants streaming from the earth. The air around us was damp, smelling of wet basements, and from within the canyon and the forest, a rhythm hung in that thick air, somewhere between heard and felt—the incessant buzzing of a billion insect wings.

Rakotondravony poked gently into the mound, looking for a *renivitsika,* or ant mother, a kind of snake that often lives within a colony's dark interior. We found no snakes, but scanning the area near the mound, Rakotondravony pointed to several plants, including palmlike trees with slender fronds. These, he explained, were another kind of guest that had made an unlikely home in the tsingy's narrow passages. They were a species common in the wet forests of eastern Madagascar but mostly absent from the much drier west. Only here, within the grikes, had the plants escaped the drying sun and roaming wildfires. The plants were just one example. There are certain frogs too, he said, whose nearest known relatives live hundreds of miles away in the eastern forests.

The difficult terrain creates still tinier refuges, where some creatures appear to have evolved in greater solitude, restricted to just a few canyons within the tsingy. John Cleese's lemur, a mouse lemur, and at least two of the pinkie-size dwarf chameleons—some of the world's smallest—illustrate this kind of micro-endemism, where evolution has tailor-fitted animals into tight niches.

Brian Fisher has traveled to the region three times to understand how these refuges formed and how they have shaped the life within them. Through DNA analysis, he is comparing ants from the tsingy region to ants in eastern Madagascar, hoping to pin down exactly when the ants, and the forests, became isolated. The results will provide clues to how animals evolve once they are shut off from other populations, and whether they respond to climate change only by retreating into refuges or by developing new traits as well. The answers, Fisher said, could have implications for the future, as human activity undermines habitats and the planet's climate changes.

Because it is remote and virtually impenetrable, development seems less likely to threaten the tsingy ecosystem than would a shift in regional weather. Lower humidity, less rainfall, increased acidity in the rain—any of these might harm the forests, even the stone itself.

"I wonder how long they could survive, these

relict forests," Fisher mused. "They could disappear very shortly. It's a fortress, but it's vulnerable. The truth is we don't know very much. We're just getting a handle on this stuff."

ON ONE OF MY LAST DAYS in the tsingy, I stood on a lookout platform scanning an expanse of spires and pinnacles, the gray stone purpling in the late afternoon. The platform had been built several years earlier for tourists, but the tourists were no longer coming. The coup had frightened them off. It was bad news for the park; 50 percent of its budget comes from fees associated with tourism. An official told me that 2008 had been a good year, but 2009 wasn't looking promising. In April 2008, 147 visitors had come to Tsingy de Bemaraha; during the same month in 2009, after the coup, there had been 12. The official wasn't sure how he'd make up the difference or what effect it would have on the reserve, on employee salaries, on the development and education programs that give poor local people reasons to care about preservation. He smiled tiredly. "We will become creative."

Not far away a troop of sifakas leaped through the pinnacle tops, clearing deep canyons, landing on razors of rock. With their bright white fur, the lemurs look like polar creatures marooned in the tropics. They move through one of the world's most formidable landscapes as though physical laws mean nothing, as though such laws are arguments made by less agile creatures to explain away their own clumsiness.

The sifakas disappeared with the light. Parrots arced through the sky, passing large, silent bats. In the canyons below, the forest flattened into a gray smudge. We climbed down and headed for camp, playing our headlamps through the trees. Thousands of eyes glinted in the darkness, orange and green jewels, the eyes of nocturnal lemurs known only here, of geckos with skins as smooth and iridescent as a trout's, of large spiders and moths, their bodies thin as shadows. The night itself was becoming a refuge, a kind of temporary continent, enclosing the stone city and all its creatures, the named and the still nameless. □

Nightfall does nothing to soften the spiny ramparts, yet cooler temperatures and rising humidity entice many nocturnal creatures to emerge. Says biologist Steven Goodman, one of the few scientists to make repeat visits, "We've just touched the surface as far as finding out what lives there."

A Harvest of

Long at the mercy of the monsoons, some Indian farmers are sculpting hillsides to capture runoff, enriching their land and lives.

By Sara Corbett · Photographs by Lynsey Addario

Villages with no watershed plan, such as Yethewadi, must depend on cascades of water from tanker trucks to refill their wells.

Water

FARMERS IN INDIA do a lot of talking about the weather—especially, it seems, when there is no weather in sight. During the month of May, when the land heats up like a furnace and most fields lie fallow, when wells have run dry and the sun taunts from its broiling perch in a cloudless sky, there is no topic more consuming—or less certain—than when and how the summer monsoon will arrive. The monsoon season, which normally starts in early June and delivers more than three-quarters of the country's annual rainfall in less than four months, will begin gently, like a deer, the farmers say, and later it will turn into a thundering elephant. Or it will start as an elephant and then turn into a deer. Or it will be erratic and annoying right through, like a chicken. In other words, nobody really knows. But still, everybody talks.

This was the case one day in 2008 when an extended family of farmers from a village called Satichiwadi climbed up to the hilltop temple of their village goddess, planning to ask her for rain. It was mid-May and 106 degrees, and Satichiwadi, a village of 83 families that sits in a parched rural valley in the state of Maharashtra, about a

A fickle monsoon sky disappoints farmers crossing the Bhima River on a Hindu pilgrimage to the city of Pandharpur. Instead of a much needed downpour, the clouds deliver a mere sprinkle.

hundred miles northeast of Mumbai, hadn't had any significant rainfall for seven months. Most of India at this point was caught in an inescapable annual wait. In New Delhi, the heat had triggered power cuts. Dust storms raced, unmitigated by moisture, across the northern states. Tanker trucks clogged the rural highways, delivering government-sponsored loads of drinking water to villages whose wells had run dry. Meanwhile, radio newscasters were just beginning to track a promising swirl of rain clouds moving over the Andaman Islands, off the southeast coast.

All day, villagers had been speculating about those distant clouds. It was gambling time for rain-dependent farmers across India. In the weeks leading up to the monsoon, many would invest a significant amount of money, often borrowed, to buy fertilizer and millet seeds, which needed to be planted ahead of the rains. There were many ways to lose this wager. A delayed monsoon likely would cause the seeds to bake and die in the ground. Or if the rain fell too hard before the seedlings took root, it might wash them all away.

"Our lives are wrapped up in the rain," explained a woman named Anusayabai Pawar, using a countrywoman's version of Marathi, the regional language. "When it comes, we have everything. When it doesn't, we have nothing."

In the meantime, everyone kept scanning the empty sky. "Like fools," said an older farmer named Yamaji Pawar, sweating beneath his white Nehru cap, "we just sit here waiting."

IF THE PEOPLE OF SATICHIWADI once believed the gods controlled the rain, they were starting to move beyond that. Even as they carried betel nuts and cones of incense up to the goddess's temple, even as one by one the village women knelt down in front of the stone idol that represented her, they seemed merely to be hedging their bets. Bhaskar Pawar, a sober-minded, mustachioed farmer in his 30s, sat on one of the low walls of the temple, watching impassively as his female relatives prayed. "Especially the younger people here understand now that it's environmental," he said.

Satichiwadi lies in India's rain shadow, an especially water-deprived swath of land that includes much of central Maharashtra. Each year after the summer monsoon pounds the west coast of India, it moves inward across the plains and bumps against the 5,000-foot peaks

Reveling in the luxury of a soaking, guests at the Wet 'N Joy theme park near Shirdi dance to a Bollywood beat. Tapping the drought-prone region's aquifer for non-essential uses diverts water from farmers who need it desperately.

of the Western Ghats, where the clouds stall out, leaving the leeward side punishingly dry.

In an effort to lessen their dependence on the monsoon, the village's residents had signed on to an ambitious, three-year watershed program designed to make more efficient use of what little rain does fall. The program was facilitated by a nonprofit group called the Watershed Organization Trust (WOTR), but the work—a major relandscaping of much of the valley—was being done by the villagers themselves. Teams of farmers spent an average of five days a week digging, moving soil, and planting seedlings along the ridgelines. WOTR, which has led similar projects in more than 200 villages in central India, paid the villagers for roughly 80 percent of the hours worked but also required every family to contribute free labor to the project every month—a deliberate move to get everyone invested.

From the vantage point of the temple, the effort was evident: Beyond the small grids of tile-roofed mud homes and the sun-crisped patchwork of dry fields, many of the russet brown hillsides had been terraced, and a number of freshly dug trenches sat waiting to catch the rain. If only, of course, the rain would come.

In Satichiwadi the anticipation was high. "Very soon," Bhaskar said, "we will know the value of this work."

COMPLEX AND CAPRICIOUS, the South Asian monsoon—widely considered the most powerful seasonal climate system on Earth, affecting nearly half the world's population—has never been easy to predict. And with global warming skewing weather patterns, it's not just the scientists who are confounded. Farmers whose families for generations have used the *Panchangam*, a thick almanac detailing the movement of the Hindu constellations, to determine when the monsoon rains are due and thus when to plant their crops, lament that their system no longer works reliably.

Sara Corbett is a contributing writer for the New York Times Magazine. *Lynsey Addario photographed Bhutan for* National Geographic *in March 2008.*

"It is a bit of a puzzle," said B. N. Goswami, director of the Indian Institute of Tropical Meteorology, based in Pune. After studying five decades of rain gauge data for central India, Goswami and his colleagues concluded that although the amount of rainfall has not changed, it is coming in shorter, more intense bursts, with fewer spells of light rain between, mirroring a larger pattern of extreme weather worldwide.

Groundwater has helped some farmers cope with erratic rains. But India's water tables are dropping precipitously, as farmers who now have access to electric pumps withdraw water faster than the monsoon can replenish it. According to the International Water Management Institute, based in Sri Lanka, half the wells once used in western India no longer function. "Thirty years ago we could strike water by digging 30 feet," said the village chief in Khandarmal, a dusty settlement of about 3,000 people perched on a ridge about 20 miles from Satichiwadi. "Now we have to go to 400 feet." Even that is chancy. Over the years the villagers have drilled a total of 500 wells. Ninety percent of them, he estimated, have gone dry.

Water shortages throw farmers into an unrelenting cycle of debt and distress, driving many—by one estimate up to a hundred million each year—to seek work in factories and distant, better irrigated fields. During the dry months, between November and May, you see them on the roads: families creaking along in bullock carts, truck taxis jammed with entire neighborhoods of people on the move. The stakes can seem impossibly high. According to government figures, the number of suicides among male farmers in Maharashtra tripled between 1995 and 2004.

One afternoon outside a sugarcane processing factory not far from Satichiwadi, I met a boy named Valmik. He was 16, with a sweet smile and out-turned ears, wearing a brown T-shirt and pants that were ripped across the seat. Standing in front of his bullock cart loaded with two tons of freshly cut sugarcane, he explained that he had driven his two-oxen cart 110 or so miles with his older brother and widowed mother to spend five months working in

INDIA'S RAIN SHADOW

Monsoon rains skip a large part of several Indian states. Clouds loaded with moist sea air deluge the western side of coastal mountains (map). When they reach the area of the Deccan basalts, they're mostly wrung out and offer only a drizzle (graphs) to farmers.

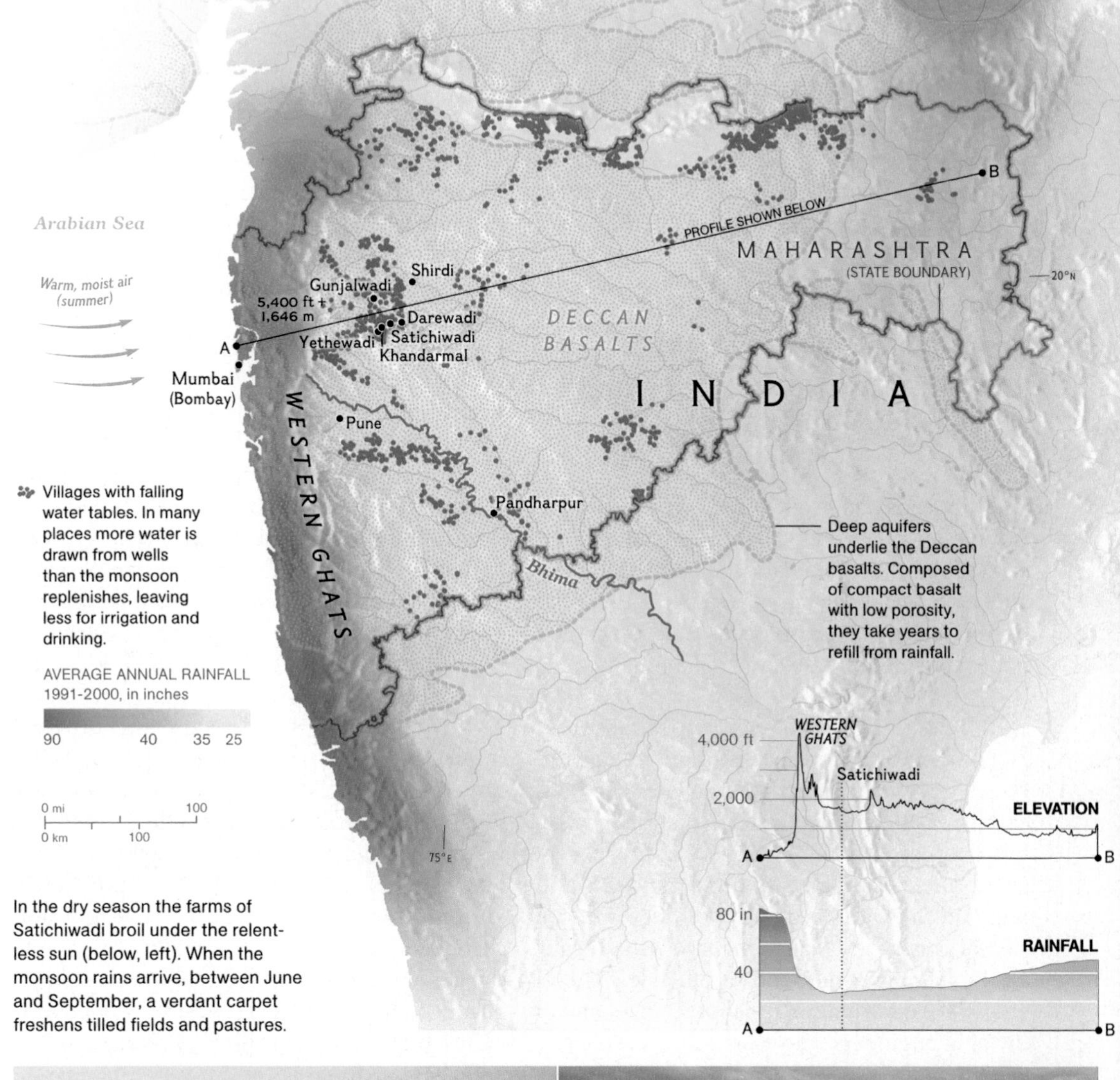

In the dry season the farms of Satichiwadi broil under the relentless sun (below, left). When the monsoon rains arrive, between June and September, a verdant carpet freshens tilled fields and pastures.

MAP: VIRGINIA W. MASON, NG STAFF. SOURCES: GROUNDWATER SURVEYS AND DEVELOPMENT AGENCY, GOVERNMENT OF MAHARASHTRA; CLIMATIC RESEARCH UNIT, UNIVERSITY OF EAST ANGLIA

the fields with a sickle. His arms and hands were heavily scarred from the work.

Speaking softly, Valmik detailed one of the crueler paradoxes of rain dependence. A year earlier his family had borrowed 40,000 rupees (about $800) from a moneylender to cover expenses such as seeds and fertilizer for their fields at home and hadn't been able to pay it back. Why? Because there hadn't been enough rain, and the seeds had broiled in the ground. What would they do when the debt was paid off? The same thing they'd done for the past three years after a season of cutting sugarcane: They would borrow again, plant more seeds, and revive their hopes for a decent monsoon.

"Where the rain runs, we make it walk; where it walks, we make it crawl," said Crispino Lobo of the Watershed Organization Trust.

GIVEN THE ENORMITY of India's water issues, encouraging single villages to revive and protect their own watersheds can seem a feeble response to a national crisis. But compared with controversial top-down, government-led efforts to build big dams and regulate the wanton drilling of deep wells, a careful grassroots effort to manage water locally can look both sensible and sustainable. When I visited Khandarmal with Ashok Sangle, one of the civil engineers who works for WOTR, the people there described a failed $500,000 development project to pump water several miles uphill from the nearest river. Sangle shook his head. "What is the logic of pulling water up a slope," he asked, "when you can more easily catch the rain as it flows down?"

The idea behind watershed development is simple: If people cut fewer trees, increase plant cover on the land, and build a well-planned series of dams and earthen terraces to divert and slow the downhill flow of rainwater, the soil has more time to absorb moisture. The terracing and new vegetation also control erosion, which keeps nutrient-rich topsoil from washing or blowing away, and this in turn boosts the productivity of agricultural land.

"Where the rain runs, we make it walk; where it walks, we make it crawl," explained Crispino Lobo, one of WOTR's founders, using an analogy the organization often employs when introducing the concepts behind watershed work to farmers. "Where it crawls, we make it sink into the ground." Runoff is reduced. The water table for the whole area rises, wells are less apt to go dry, and especially with some simultaneous efforts to use water more efficiently, everybody needs to worry less about when it will rain again.

The benefits—at least hypothetically—spool outward from here. More productive farmland means more food and better health for the villagers, and it opens the possibility of growing cash crops. "The first thing people do when their watershed regenerates and their income goes up," Lobo said, "is to take their kids out of the fields and put them in school."

Lobo began working on water issues in the early 1980s through a development program funded by the German government. WOTR is now directed by Marcella D'Souza, a medical doctor and Lobo's wife, whose efforts to involve women in watershed redevelopment have earned international recognition. They believe there is an important emotional dimension to watershed work as well. "If people are able to improve the land and restore the soil, you start seeing a change in how they see themselves," Lobo said. "The land reflects some hope back at them."

To be clear, this is not always easy. Since the late 1990s, both the Indian government and a variety of nongovernmental organizations have funneled some $500 million annually into redeveloping watersheds in drought-prone rural areas. But experts say many such endeavors have fallen short of their goals or proved unsustainable, in large part because they have focused too much on the technical aspects of improving a watershed and too little on navigating the complex social dynamics of farming villages. In other words, no effort gets very far without a lot of hands-on

During a three-year watershed project, residents of Satichiwadi dig a trench to catch rain as it races downhill. Landless villagers are paid for this work. Landowners, whose fields will benefit from the resulting rise in the water table, donate some of their labor.

cooperation. And if you're wondering what could possibly be so complex about a smallish group of marginal farmers living in the middle of nowhere, you should go to Satichiwadi and spend some time with the Kales and the Pawars.

SATICHIWADI LIES several miles off a two-lane road that crosses a high, semiarid plain dotted with meager-looking farms and drought-resistant neem trees. The road to the village, completed last year, remains little more than an axle-smashing series of dirt switchbacks descending some 600 vertical feet from the high bluffs to the flat valley floor. Many of the villagers still come and go the old-fashioned way, making a 45-minute, sweaty hike up a vertiginous footpath.

Members of the Pawar family like to say they got here first, about a hundred years ago, when this was a mostly uninhabited, forested place, and great-grandfather Soma Pawar, a nomadic shepherd belonging to the Thakar tribe, made his way down from the high buttes and liked what he saw. Sometime after that—precisely how long is in dispute—great-grandfather Goma Genu Kale, also a Thakar, is said to have ambled in and taken up residence as well.

For a time the Kale and Pawar families got along just fine, living close together in a small group of thatched-roof, mud-brick homes built near the temple. Working together, they cleared trees and tilled the land to grow rice and other grains. Then, about 40 or 50 years ago, the Kales abruptly moved to the other side of the valley. The reason is also in dispute: The Kales say they simply got tired of tromping the half mile or so back and forth to their millet fields. The Pawars say, somewhat huffily, that the Kales got sick of the Pawars.

Whatever the case, the two families—despite being separated by no more than 500 yards of fields—stopped *(Continued on page 126)*

Pooled amid the system of trenches and dams created in Satichiwadi, rainwater soaks slowly into the ground. That moisture will help sustain crops and increase grazing for herds of cattle and goats.

The Karande family grows water-intensive onions as a cash crop, benefiting from more than a decade of land contouring around Darewadi. Before, they subsisted on millet scratched from parched fields.

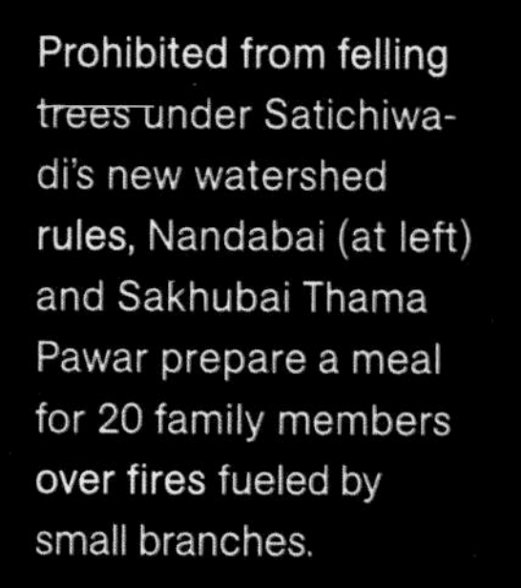

Prohibited from felling trees under Satichiwadi's new watershed rules, Nandabai (at left) and Sakhubai Thama Pawar prepare a meal for 20 family members over fires fueled by small branches.

talking. They held their own independent holy weeks to celebrate the goddess Sati and pointedly stopped attending one another's weddings. The Pawars stopped calling the Kales by name, referring to them instead as the "Fed Up People." The hamlet where the Kales now live is known simply as *Vaitagwadi*, Fed Up Town.

As Satichiwadi's harmony deteriorated, another kind of diminishment began. Sheep and cows trampled the grassland; the last of the trees disappeared. Crops too began to falter. Farmers gave up growing rice, which required so much water. By March each year, most of the wells across the valley had dried up.

Darewadi's farmers are getting their first taste of prosperity, growing onions, tomatoes, and lentils and selling the surplus.

With both food and income scarce, villagers started migrating to work on sugarcane plantations, on road crews, and in brick factories. "If you had come even three years ago during the dry season," Sitaram Kale, a farmer who also owns a small shop in Satichiwadi, told me, "you would have found only very old people and very small children living here."

The villagers did not easily come around to the idea that they could work together and revive the valley. Getting them to set aside their differences took months of meetings, several exploratory "exposure visits" to other villages where WOTR's watershed programs had been successful, and the diligent attention of a high-energy young social worker named Rohini Raosaheb Hande, who hiked the path into Satichiwadi every other day for six months. Hande was the second social worker WOTR had sent to Satichiwadi; the first had quit after a few weeks. "She told me it was a place without hope," Hande recalled. "Nobody would even talk to her."

Such resistance is common. In the village of Darewadi, where the watershed work was completed in 2001, one villager had chased WOTR employees away with an ax. Because the organization encourages simultaneous social reconfiguration and environmental change, its efforts often initially rub farmers the wrong way. WOTR mandates, for example, that village-level water decisions include women, landless people, and members of lower castes, all of whom might ordinarily be excluded. To give the local greenery a chance to recover, villagers must also agree to a multiyear ban on free-grazing their animals and cutting trees for firewood. Finally, they must trust the potential benefits of watershed work enough to sign on to the sheer tedium it entails—three to five years spent using pickaxes and shovels to move dirt from one spot to another to redirect the flow of rainwater.

In Darewadi an elderly farmer named Chimaji Avahad, who lives with his extended family in a brightly painted two-room home hemmed in by sorghum fields, recalled the early difficulties of adjusting to the new rules. He was taken aback, he told me, by the talkative women who filled his life. "Each one of them—my wife, daughters, daughters-in-law, and even granddaughters—has an opinion," he said, amused. His wife, Nakabai, a tiny woman with a face wizened by years working in the fields, immediately chimed in, "It was a very good change."

A walk around Darewadi confirms this. By all accounts a grim and waterless place before the project began more than a decade ago, it now boasts bushes and trees and fields of wild grass. The village's wells now remain full, even at the height of the dry season. With more water, Darewadi's farmers are getting their first taste of prosperity, moving from producing only enough millet to feed themselves to growing onions, tomatoes, pomegranates, and lentils and selling the surplus in nearby market towns. Avahad now puts about 5,000 rupees (about a hundred dollars) a year in the bank. Darewadi's women have used their new influence to ban the sale of alcohol and also have formed women's savings groups—a common feature of WOTR projects—that collect a small monthly fee and in turn loan money to members who need it to

In the village of Gunjalwadi, one-year-old Sarika Walunj's monthly weigh-in records her growth. The watershed program here has led to more crops and better nutrition and to the increased prosperity that supports this day care center, staffed by local women.

pay for weddings or veterinary care or the solar lights that now dot the village at night.

WHEN I RETURNED TO SATICHIWADI in January, the villagers were finding some hope in their own land. The young trees on the ridgetops were green and thriving. The hills and fields had been contoured with small dams and trenches, looking like tidy ripples arcing across a brownish pond. Bhaskar Pawar—the farmer who had sat in the temple with me eight months earlier, waiting to see whether the watershed work would pay off—excitedly reported that the water level in the village wells was about ten feet higher than normal. And this was a good thing, because the monsoon had once again confounded the villagers. Not a drop had fallen over the valley during the month of June or in the first three weeks of July. Their millet seeds had withered and died. "It was a miserable time," Bhaskar recalled.

And yet when the rain did come—in torrents in late July—they were ready to catch the water and put it to use. They'd spent the fall months harvesting tomatoes. Now they were working on onions and sorghum. And they were also harvesting something less tangible: a newfound, tenuous harmony.

One morning I watched as Sitaram Kale, the shopkeeper and one of nine members of the Village Watershed Development Committee, rode his bike over to the Pawars' settlement to spread the word about a watershed-related meeting to be held later in the dusty schoolyard on his side of town. He passed the news to a voluble, grandmotherly woman named Chandrakhanta Pawar, who disseminated it by ducking her head into several of her neighbors' homes, assuring that each would come and participate. "There's a meeting later this morning over in Fed Up Town," she announced. "One of the Fed Up People just came over to say so." □

WHEN CROCS RULED

This vigilant yellow eye belongs to a Nile crocodile, a fearsome hunter perfected by epochs of evolutionary trial and error. Over the course of 240 million years, these predators and their kin have come to rule the netherworld between dry land and deep water. But as their habitats dwindle, many croc species face an uncertain future.

Eighty million years ago *Deinosuchus* (at right) would have hunted much like its modern descendant, the American alligator, using stealth and a viselike bite to snatch a 30-foot *Albertosaurus* from the shallows and drag it into deep water.

RAÚL MARTÍN

BY MEL WHITE

IN THE SUMMER OF 2008 an American crocodile left Florida's Biscayne Bay, swam along a yacht-lined canal through the upscale neighborhood of Coral Gables, and took up residence on the campus of the University of Miami, where it occasionally interrupted its sunbathing on the banks of Lake Osceola to munch on a turtle. The snaggletoothed croc was a daily reminder to students that they'd chosen a school in sunny, subtropical Florida and not in, say, Iowa.

This wasn't the first crocodile to appear on campus, but it became the most famous. People took to calling it Donna, after university president and former Cabinet member Donna Shalala—this despite the fact that it turned out to be a male. Donna occasionally basked on the grass just yards from the university pub, prompting the relocation of a few picnic tables but causing no further disruption.

Early on October 1 someone killed Donna, an act that outraged students and faculty and broke both state and federal laws: The American crocodile is classified as endangered by Florida law and threatened by federal law. A month after the crime, police arrested a man and a teenage boy, who allegedly wanted the skull as a trophy.

Mel White is a frequent contributor. His articles have covered, among others, pelicans, jaguars, Philippine eagles, and the elusive ivory-billed woodpecker.

It's tempting to use Donna as a metaphor for the plight of the world's 23 recognized species of crocodilians, a group of related reptiles including crocodiles, alligators, caimans, and gharials. Having endured millions of years of planetary climate change, tectonic-plate musical chairs, and other ecological vicissitudes, they face a new challenge to their survival: us.

In the 1970s the population of crocodiles in Florida may have dropped to fewer than 400 individuals. The state's booming human population had crowded them out of most of the protected saltwater bays where they once lived, and many were killed by poachers for their hides, stuffed for museum displays, or captured for live exhibits.

An early croc forerunner, *Desmatosuchus* inhabited low-lying floodplains in Texas, New Mexico, and Arizona in the late Triassic. Its bony plates, or osteoderms, are also found in living crocodilians.

In the years since, conservation measures have led to a rebound in Florida crocs, which may now number some 2,000. "Crocodile management isn't rocket science," says Steve Klett, manager of Florida's Crocodile Lake National Wildlife Refuge. "If you protect their habitat and protect them from being killed, they will respond. The big issue now is the restricted range: Once they've occupied all the available habitat, where will they go?"

In Donna's case, to an urban area where he shouldn't have been living—except that there was probably no better alternative.

TODAY'S CROCODILIANS are often said to be survivors from the age of dinosaurs. That's true as far as it goes: Modern crocs have been around for some 80 million years. But they're only a small sampling of the crocodilian relatives that once roamed the planet—and, in fact, once ruled it.

Crurotarsans (a term paleontologists use to include all croc relatives) appeared about 240 million years ago, generally at the same time as dinosaurs. During the Triassic period, crocodile ancestors radiated into a wide array of terrestrial forms, from slender, long-legged animals something like wolves to huge, fearsome predators at the top of the food chain. Some, like the animal called *Effigia,* walked at least part of the time on two legs and were probably herbivores. So dominant were crurotarsans on land that

PHOTO: IRA BLOCK; 16-FOOT REPLICA SKELETON PHOTOGRAPHED AT PETRIFIED FOREST NATIONAL PARK

CROC EVOLUTION The early predecessors of crocodilians, along with pterosaurs, nonavian dinosaurs, and birds, evolved from a common ancestor, then diversified spectacularly (below). In myriad sizes and shapes, they established niches in marine and terrestrial habitats worldwide and feasted on everything from flowers to flesh. Supreme adaptability helped crocs survive many global extinctions, including the one 65 million years ago that killed off pterosaurs and dinosaurs.

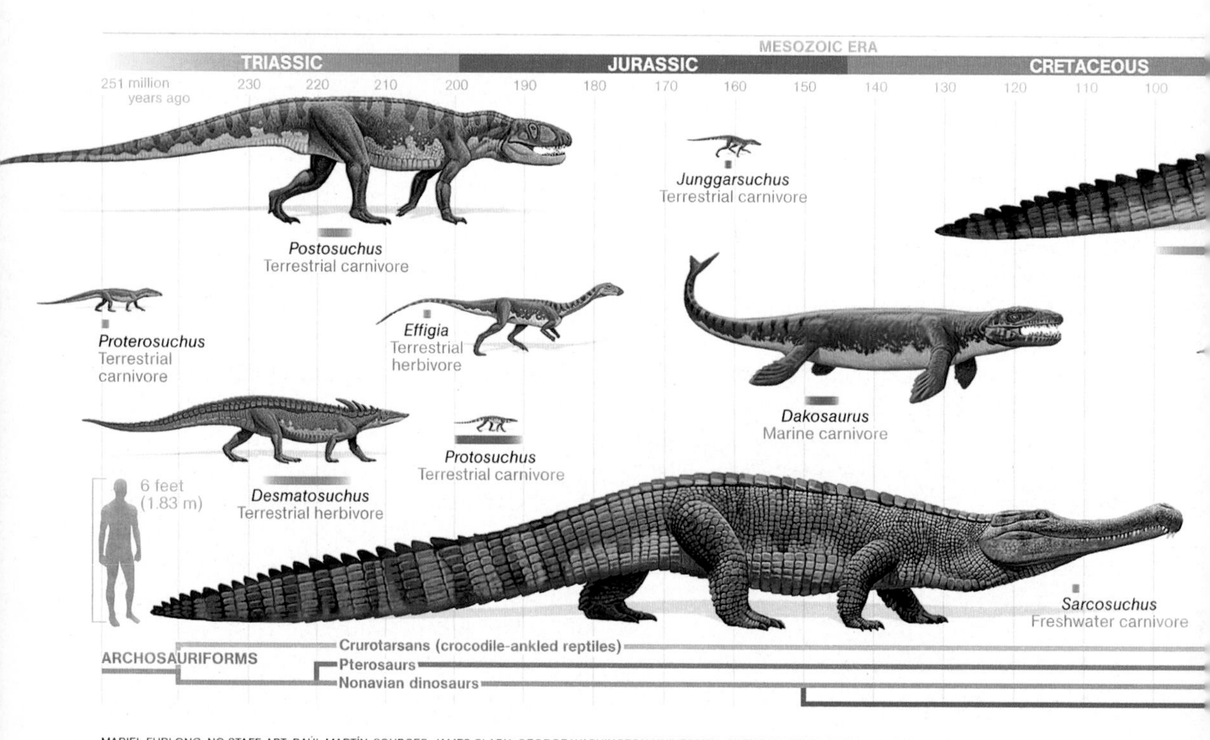

MARIEL FURLONG, NG STAFF. ART: RAÚL MARTÍN. SOURCES: JAMES CLARK, GEORGE WASHINGTON UNIVERSITY; CHRISTOPHER BROCHU, UNIVERSITY OF IOWA; DIEGO POL, MUSEO PALEONTOLÓGICO EGIDIO FERUGLIO, ARGENTINA; ALAN TURNER, STONY BROOK UNIVERSITY; STERLING NESBITT, AMERICAN MUSEUM OF NATURAL HISTORY

Famous for its bone-crushing jaws, a Nile crocodile (above) also dominates with the help of powerful legs, which allow it to strike quickly and pull down adult wildebeests. Its tail helps propel its surprising leap, demonstrated in Bazoulé, Burkina Faso (above left), where people have worshipped crocs for centuries.

CENOZOIC ERA
TERTIARY

90 80 70 60 50 40 30 20 10 Today

Stomatosuchus
Freshwater carnivore

Nile crocodile
Freshwater carnivore

Pristichampsus
Terrestrial carnivore

Stratiotosuchus
Terrestrial carnivore

Simosuchus
Terrestrial herbivore

Gharial
Freshwater carnivore

Arambourgisuchus
Freshwater carnivore

Alligator
Freshwater carnivore

○ First modern crocodilians
Extinction event
Birds

MODERN CROCODILIANS

The three families living today are easily distinguished.

Crocodiles: Most but not all lower teeth are visible when mouth is closed.

Gharials: Long, very narrow snout with many narrow teeth exposed when mouth is closed; males have a bulbous nose.

Alligators and caimans: Most have no lower teeth showing when mouth is closed.

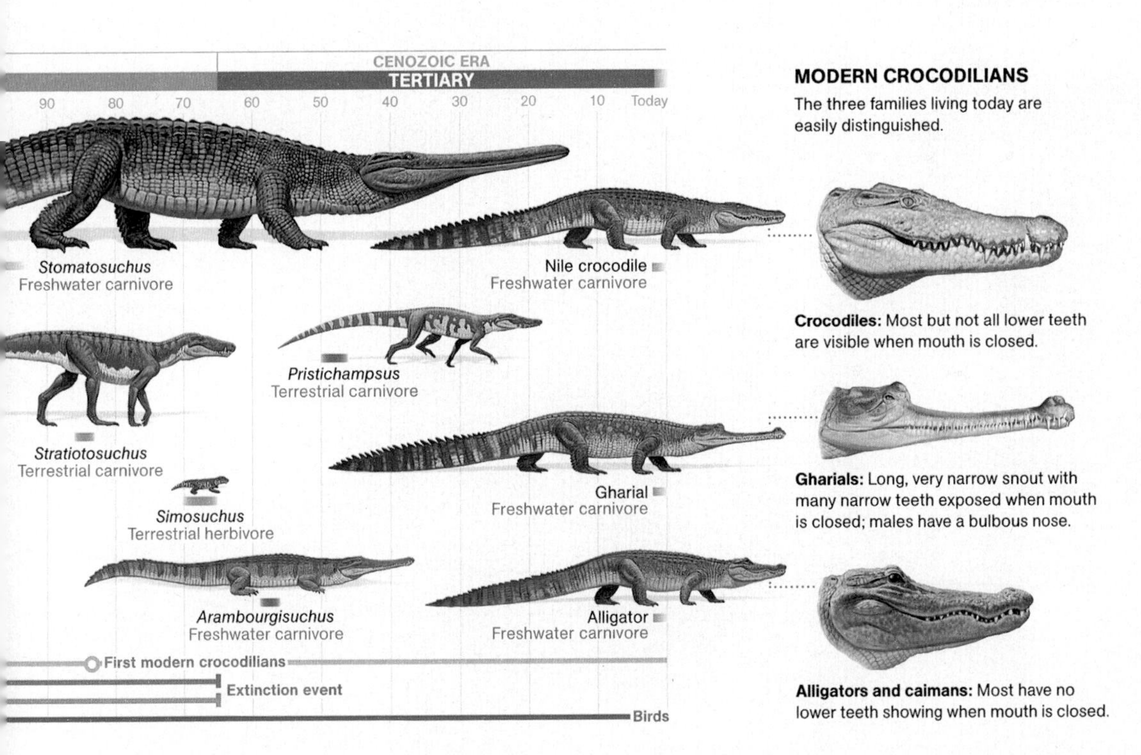

TYRONE TURNER

Armed Louisianans snare an eight-foot alligator on a chicken-baited hook. "It's like pulling in a log," says a hunter, "until the alligator sees you. Then the battle begins." The state manages a healthy annual harvest of some 34,000 wild and 240,000 farm-raised alligators. Last year the hides and meat brought in nearly $60 million.

CROC WORLD Living crocodilians, which include two species of alligators, six kinds of caimans, 14 types of crocodiles, and the lone species of gharial, all reside within 2,600 miles of the Equator, though their ancestors ranged nearly from Pole to Pole. Some species, such as the American alligator and Nile crocodile, are thriving, but many others are declining as humans expand into croc habitat. Some, such as the African dwarf crocodile (above), are hunted for their meat. A few species, notably the gharial, may go extinct within a decade in the wild.

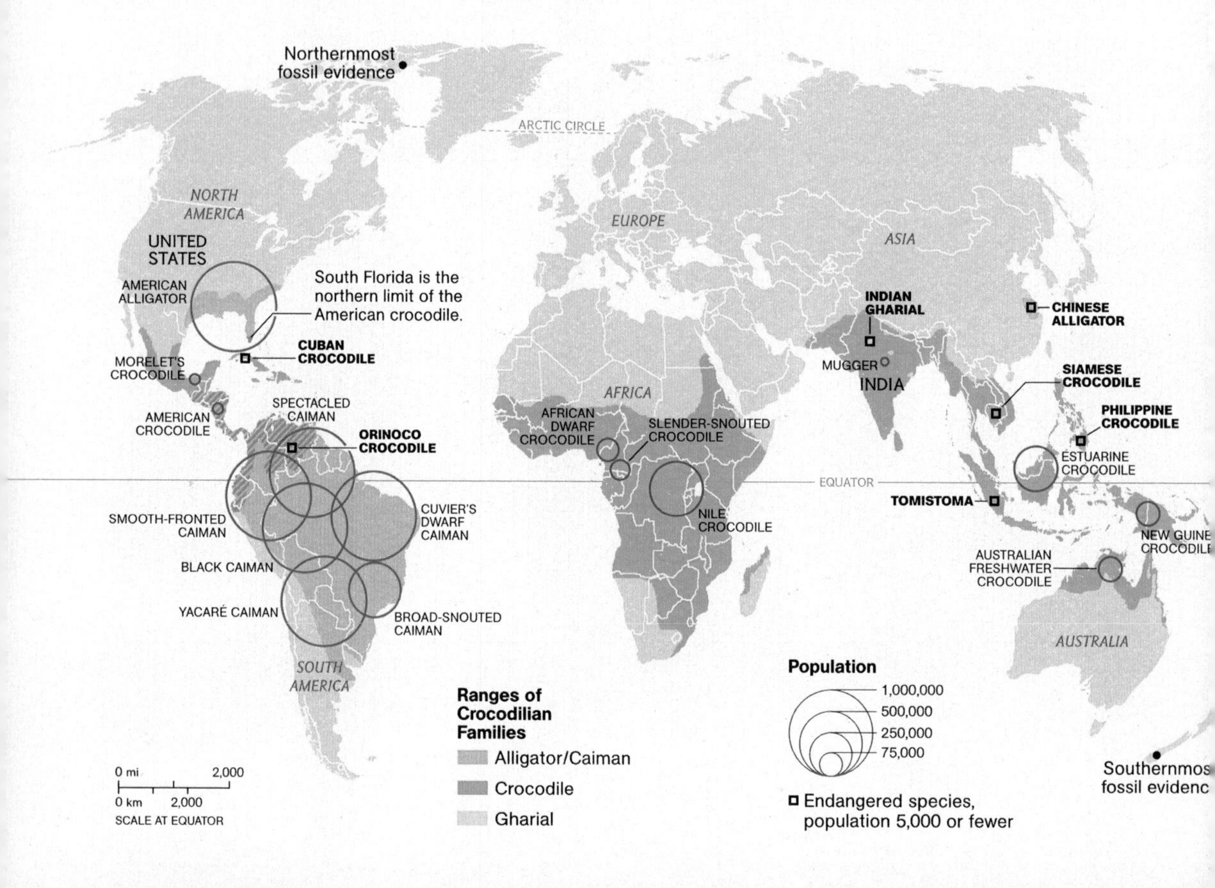

WITH LAND-BASED DINOSAURS AND SEA MONSTERS GONE, WHY DIDN'T CROCS TAKE OVER THE EARTH ONCE AND FOR ALL?

dinosaurs were limited in the ecological niches they could occupy, staying mostly small in size and uncommon in number.

At the end of the Triassic, about 200 million years ago, an unknown cataclysm wiped out most crurotarsans. With the land cleared of their competitors, dinosaurs took over. At the same time, huge swimming predators such as plesiosaurs had evolved in the ocean, leaving little room for interlopers. The crocs that survived took on a new diversity of forms, but eventually they lived, as their descendants do today, in the only places they could: rivers, swamps, and marshes.

Restricted ecological niches may have limited the creatures' evolutionary opportunities—but also may have saved them. Many croc species survived the massive K-T (Cretaceous-Tertiary) extinction 65 million years ago, when an asteroid dealt a death blow to the dinosaurs (except for birds, now viewed as latter-day dinosaurs) and a broad range of other life on land and in the oceans. No one knows why crocs lived when so much died, but their freshwater habitat is one explanation: Freshwater species generally did better during the K-T event than did marine animals, which lost extensive shallow habitat as sea level dropped. Their wide-ranging diet and cold-blooded ability to go long periods without food may have helped as well.

With land-based dinosaurs and sea monsters gone, why didn't crocs take over the Earth once and for all? By then mammals had begun their evolutionary march toward world domination. Over time the most divergent lines of crocs died out, leaving the squat-bodied, short-legged forms we're familiar with.

"THE MAIN CHANGE in recent crocodilian conservation has been the decline in illegal hunting for skins," says John Thorbjarnarson of the Wildlife Conservation Society, a leading expert on the group. It's been replaced by legally managed ranching and harvesting, allowing some species to rebound. "Whereas 20 years ago there may have been 15 or 20 species that were listed as endangered," Thorbjarnarson says, "now there are really only seven, all reflecting the loss of most of their habitat."

Species such as the Chinese alligator and the Philippine crocodile have virtually no natural habitat left, squeezed out of their former ranges by agricultural and urban growth. And even species that have responded positively to conservation measures face a problem that's a larger scale version of Donna's: contact, and often conflict, with humans.

The Indian gharial, a skinny-snouted species that once ranged from Pakistan to Myanmar, suffered serious population declines in the mid-20th century. Recovery in the 1980s and 1990s, thanks to decreased poaching and establishment of protected areas, gave conservationists reason to believe it was out of trouble. But recent surveys have shown that gharial numbers have once again crashed, this time to critically endangered status.

Gharials eat only fish and require a specialized habitat of swiftly flowing rivers with sandy banks. Factors in their decrease include persecution by fishermen (who see them as competitors), drowning in fishing nets, and destruction of their habitat by sand mining and other human activities. In addition, a significant gharial population on India's Chambal River was decimated between December 2007 and February 2008 by what some biologists believe was pollution. The wild population of gharials has shrunk to a few hundred individuals living only in India and Nepal.

Some crocodilians found in remote parts of the world are not in immediate danger, and others such as the American alligator have made dramatic recoveries. But it remains to be seen how many can endure in a world where their wetland homes are coveted by people from subsistence farmers to golf course designers—and where some species make themselves less than welcome by eating pets and even people.

Thought to be an origin of ancient dragon myths, crocodilians and their ancestors have faced nearly unimaginable changes to the planet and found ways to adapt to them all. As the pace of environmental change quickens, though, their greatest challenges are yet to come. □

PHOTO: FRANS LEMMENS, PETER ARNOLD, INC
MAP: LISA R. RITTER, NG STAFF. SOURCE: ADAM BRITTON, BIG GECKO CROCODILIAN RESEARCH

BOARCROC This 20-foot-long meat-eater—its prey likely included dinosaurs—had an armored snout it could use for ramming and three sets of fangs for slicing. Eye sockets turned forward enhanced stereoscopic vision to aid in hunting; large, well-developed muscles gave the jaw extra biting power.

ART: TODD MARSHALL. PHOTO: MIKE HETTWER

STRANGE CROCS OF THE SAHARA

SINCE THE 1990s, with my teams of researchers and students, I have combed the Sahara for evidence of creatures great and small that lived with the dinosaurs.

My recent expeditions have revealed a treasure trove of crocs that populated Gondwana—the landmass that comprised today's southern continents—some 110 million years ago. Some were plant-eating dwarfs, others dinosaur-eating giants. Now their fossilized bones poke from parched Saharan landscapes, from windswept cliffs in Morocco to barren dune fields in Niger.

In some ways the fossils we have found remind me of the crocodilians alive today. All had textured skull bones and slow-growing body armor that absorbed heat while the animals basked in the sun. Some resemble mammals, with erect limbs for fleet-footed pursuit of prey on land; teeth divided into incisors, canines, and postcanines; and forward-pointing eyes. Nicknames for the monstrous BoarCroc (left) and the more diminutive three-foot-long RatCroc, DogCroc, and DuckCroc (right) capture those likenesses.

So what were the lifestyles of these creatures? Were they landlubbers, or were they predominantly aquatic like their kin, the crocs that remain today? I found a clue on a trip to northern Australia. The freshwater crocs there run so fast they actually gallop. At full speed on land they move in a sinuous, up-and-down motion like a running mammal. At water's edge their tails suddenly start to move side to side like a fish, propelling them underwater.

I closed in on a new perspective. My African crocs appeared to have had both upright, agile legs for bounding overland and a versatile tail for paddling in water. Perhaps that lay at the crux of their evolution and drove the explosion of Cretaceous crocs across Gondwana that began some 145 million years ago.

Under the noses of the dinosaurs, crocs evolved into ferocious predators and pint-size plant-eaters with a dual locomotor capability, best seen today in Australia's freshwater crocs. A distinctive survival strategy had emerged that even a monstrous asteroid could not completely erase. *—Paul Sereno*

RatCroc: A pair of buckteeth in the lower jaw may have allowed this croc to burrow in the ground for tubers.

DogCroc: With differentiated teeth and a soft nose pointing forward, this omnivore may have escaped from predators on its lanky legs.

DuckCroc: A broad, overhanging snout and hook-shaped teeth may have helped this croc catch small fish or worms in shallow water.

WHEN CROCS ATE DINOSAURS

Some 110 million years ago precursors of today's crocodiles ruled Earth. Explorer-in-Residence Paul Sereno brings a lost Cretaceous world to life on **National Geographic Channel, November 21 at 9 p.m. in the U.S.**

Trace croc evolution with an interactive time line at **ngm.com/crocs.**

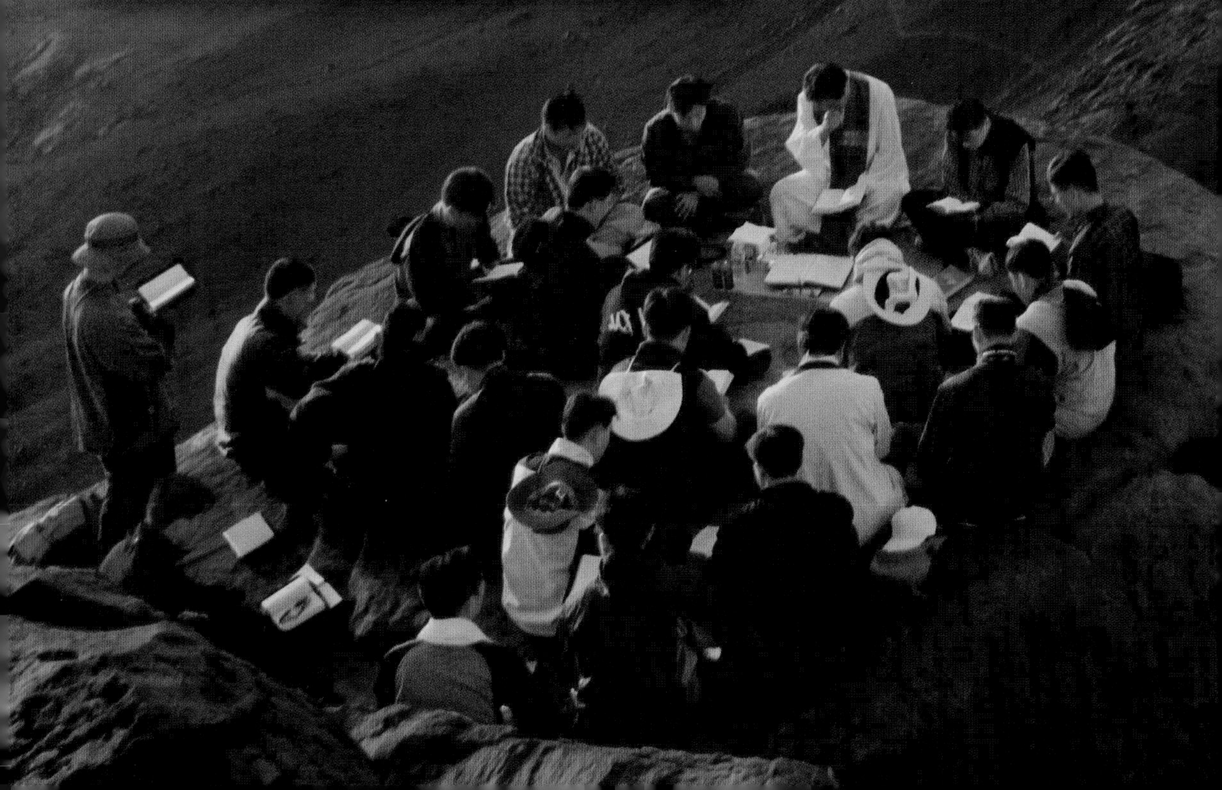

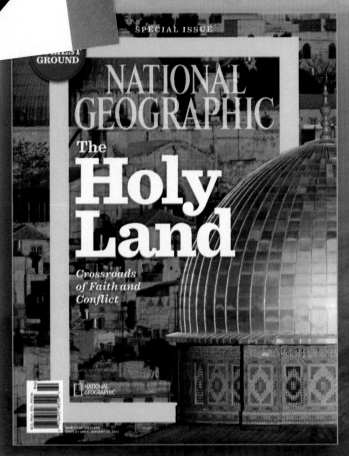

Inspire Future Generations

John-Joseph van Haelewyn

John McCallister included National Geographic in his estate plans.

An avid traveler and horticulturist, John McCallister was introduced to National Geographic when his aunt sent him a gift subscription to the magazine in the 1940s. "I like everything about National Geographic, what it stands for, and what it accomplishes," John says.

Now retired, John spends his time taking continuing education classes, landscaping his garden, and frequenting art museums, theatre performances, and concerts. John made a bequest gift as a way to support the things he holds dear. "I included National Geographic in my will because I want the Society to be around for future generations," he says.

For more information about how to include us in your estate plans, or to let us know that you have already done so, please contact the Office of Estate Planning.

NATIONAL GEOGRAPHIC

Office of Estate Planning
1145 17th Street NW
Washington, DC 20036

(800) 226 - 4438
plannedgiftinfo@ngs.org
www.nationalgeographic.org/donate

The National Geographic Society is a 501(c)(3), tax-exempt organization.

Charitable Gift Annuities may not be available in every state. Please call for availability.

Card to cut off and mail in

- ○ Yes! Please send me information on how to include National Geographic in my will
- ○ I have already included National Geographic in my will
- ○ Please send me information on a National Geographic charitable gift annuity

Birthdate(s) ______________________

Minimum age 45. *Payments begin at age 65*

Name ______________________

Address ______________________

____

Phone ______________________

Email ______________________

Mail to: National Geographic Office of Estate Planning
1145 17th Street NW, Washington, DC 20036

Ed Kashi gets reflective inside a trinket shop in Damascus.

ON ASSIGNMENT **Scenes From Syria** Taking a picture of himself in a mirror provided a moment of levity for Ed Kashi (above) in Syria. Much of the rest of his time there, things were more tense. "Our driver had been questioned about who I was," says the photographer, who also recalls being followed by a mysterious white Peugeot one afternoon. Kashi spent nearly five weeks with *National Geographic* Senior Editor Don Belt covering the country for this issue's story. They met with President Bashar al Assad (left, at right, with Belt) at his office in Damascus, where the leader spoke with them about politics, current events, and his childhood. "The Syria Bashar inherited faces huge problems that were decades in the making, so he's got a lot on his plate," says Belt. "Even so, I found him remarkably approachable and articulate."

Society Updates

PRESIDENTIAL GIFT
Since World War II, the National Geographic Society has given custom map cabinets to every President of the United States. President Barack Obama (above, with White House staffer Phil Schiliro) received his in the Oval Office in June.

NG CHANNEL
A team of experts goes to unprecedented lengths to learn about the world's largest predatory fish in *Expedition Great White.* Tune in to the National Geographic Channel on November 16 at 9 p.m. for a close-up of the mighty shark.

SPECIAL ISSUE
The Holy Land takes readers to the birthplace of three great faiths: Judaism, Christianity, and Islam. Find it in stores and online at *ngm.com/holyland* on November 3 ($10.99).

GeoPuzzle Answers

F	I	L	M	■	L	A	S	T	■	C	A	R	P	S
I	D	E	A	■	E	D	N	A	■	E	L	I	O	T
T	A	I	L	S	F	R	O	M	■	N	O	L	T	E
■	■	■	■	P	A	I	R	S	■	T	H	E	T	A
T	H	E	C	R	Y	P	T	■	X	R	A	Y	E	D
H	O	S	E	A	■	■	■	K	A	A	■	S	R	S
A	S	A	L	T	V	E	H	I	C	L	E	■	■	■
W	E	S	T	■	I	N	S	E	T	■	D	S	O	S
■	■	■	S	U	R	V	I	V	O	R	G	I	L	T
S	O	S	■	N	A	Y	■	■	■	E	E	N	I	E
T	R	I	B	A	L	■	W	R	A	P	S	O	N	G
O	I	L	E	R	■	S	H	U	L	A	■	■	■	■
R	E	A	L	M	■	H	A	R	E	D	R	Y	E	R
E	N	G	L	E	■	A	L	A	R	■	Y	A	L	U
S	T	E	E	D	■	M	E	L	T	■	E	M	I	T

world beat

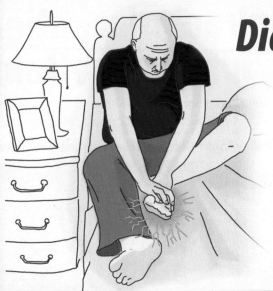

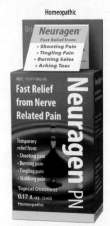

EVENTS & OPPORTUNITIES • ADVERTISING & PROMOTIONS

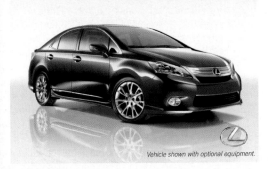

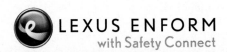

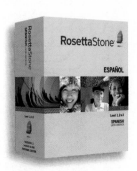

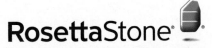

HEAT SURGE™ *Fireless* Flame™

How It Works: The HEAT SURGE miracle heater is a work of engineering genius from the China coast so advanced, you simply plug it into any standard outlet. It uses only about 9¢ of electric an hour on the standard setting. Yet, it produces up to an amazing 5,119 BTU's on the high setting. So watch out, a powerful on board hi-tech heat turbine silently forces hot air out into the room from the vent so you feel the bone soothing heat instantly. It even has certification of Underwriters Laboratories coveted UL listing. It also comes with a limited full year replacement or money back warranty less shipping plus a 30-Day Satisfaction Guarantee. OH and FL resident transactions require the remittance of applicable sales tax. Sorry no shipments to MA residents.

c UL us
LISTED: E322174

Hot air only comes out of the top vent
The hi-tech silent heat turbine takes in cold air

How to get 2 free heaters

The National Toll Free Hotlines are now open. All those who beat the 7-day order deadline to cover the cost of the Amish made Fireplace Mantle and shipping get the HEAT SURGE miracle heater free.

A strict limit of 2 per household has been imposed. Since some home woodworkers want to build their own mantle piece, they are letting people get the imported miracle heater alone for just $249. Or, with the Amish made mantle you get the miracle heater free.

Use the map below to locate the weather zone you live in and call the Hotline number for your zone.

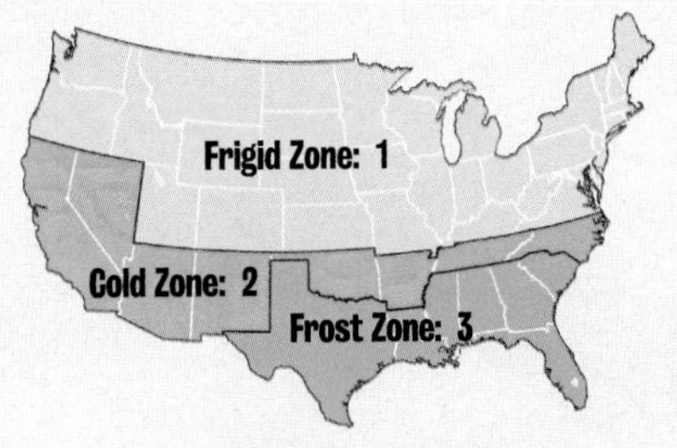
Frigid Zone: 1
Cold Zone: 2
Frost Zone: 3

ON THEIR WAY: Christmas orders have turned country roads into pipelines to the big city delivery system. Everybody wants a fireplace that comes fully assembled with a handmade Amish mantle in oak or cherry finish and gets delivered by truck right to your door. All you do is plug it in.

Claim Code: FP9687

EVERYONE LIVING IN THE	EVERYONE LIVING IN THE	EVERYONE LIVING IN THE
Frigid Zone: 1	**Cold Zone: 2**	**Frost Zone: 3**
START CALLING AT 8:00 A.M. TODAY	START CALLING AT 8:30 A.M. TODAY	START CALLING AT 9:00 A.M. TODAY
1-866-815-7004	**1-866-815-7110**	**1-866-815-7112**

FOR HEAT SURGE, LLC 8000 FREEDOM AVE., N. CANTON OH 44720

ost of the miracle heater is ee.

This free giveaway is the est way to slash heating ills and stay warm this ll and winter. The HEAT URGE Roll-n-Glow Fireace gives you zone heatg and all the beauty and armth of a built-in fireplace ut rolls from room-to-room it can also save you a ton f money on heating bills.

Even people in California nd Florida are flocking to et them so they may never have to turn on their furnace all winter. And since it uses only about 9 cents of electric an hour on the standard setting, the potential savings are absolutely incredible.

"We are making sure no one gets left out, but you better hurry because entire communities of Amish craftsmen are straining to keep up with demands. For now, we are staying out of the large national retail stores in order to let readers have two per household just as long as they call before the deadline," confirms Miller.

It's a really smart decision to get two right now because for only the next 7 days you get both miracle heaters free. That's like putting five hundred bucks right in your pocket and you can save even more money on your monthly heating bills.

"Everyone's calling to get one but those who are getting their Christmas shopping done are surprising the whole family by getting two. So when lines are busy keep trying or log onto amishfireplaces.com. We promise to get to every call. Then we can have a delivery truck out to your door right away with your beautiful Heat Surge Roll-n-Glow Fireplace," Miller said.

"You'll instantly feel bone soothing heat in any room. You will never have to be cold again," he said.

On the worldwide web:
www.amishfireplaces.com

Rolls anywhere to throw an instant heat wave with no chimney, no vents, no wood and no smoke

EASILY ROLLS ANYWHERE: This is the portable oll-n-Glow® Fireplace that asily rolls from bedroom o living room to keep you varm. No vents, no chimney nd no tools. Just plug it in.

SAVES ON BILLS: Everyone can get low bills and stay warm and cozy. The Roll-n-Glow Fireplace saves a ton of money and makes your front room look like a million bucks.

SAFE FLAME: The *Fireless* Flame looks so real it fools everyone but there is no real fire. That makes the flame window safe to the touch under the watchful eye of a parent. It's where the kids will play and the cat and dog will sleep.

FREE: Get this $249 miracle heater free. It is being given away free to all who beat the 7-day order deadline for your choice of the oak or cherry finish Amish Mantles. The free heater comes already encased.

Abridged An ancient Roman bridge spanned the Wadi al Murr near Mosul, Iraq, in the 1920s. Credited to German archaeologist Max von Oppenheim, this image never ran in the *Geographic*—nor did his manuscript for a story about his work at Tell Halaf, Syria, found with it in the photographic file. Von Oppenheim discovered the site (which dates from the sixth millennium B.C.) in 1899 and conducted excavations there over the next three decades. He shipped several treasures from the dig home to Berlin for exhibition in his personal museum, but many were destroyed in an Allied bombing raid in 1943. Objects salvaged from the rubble have recently been restored and are scheduled to go on display next year. *—Margaret G. Zackowitz*

Flashback Archive Find all the photos at **ngm.com.**

PHOTO: MAX VON OPPENHEIM, NATIONAL GEOGRAPHIC STOCK

NATIONAL GEOGRAPHIC (ISSN 0027-9358) PUBLISHED MONTHLY BY THE NATIONAL GEOGRAPHIC SOCIETY, 1145 17TH ST. NW, WASHINGTON, DC 20036. ONE YEAR MEMBERSHIP: $34.00 U.S. DELIVERY, $38.00 TO CANADA, $49.50 TO INTERNATIONAL ADDRESSES. SINGLE ISSUE: $7.00 U.S. DELIVERY, $10.00 CANADA, $15.00 INTERNATIONAL. (ALL PRICES IN U.S. FUNDS; INCLUDES SHIPPING AND HANDLING.) PERIODICALS POSTAGE PAID AT WASHINGTON, DC, AND ADDITIONAL MAILING OFFICES. POSTMASTER: SEND ADDRESS CHANGES TO NATIONAL GEOGRAPHIC, PO BOX 63002, TAMPA, FL 33663. IN CANADA, AGREEMENT NUMBER 40063649, RETURN UNDELIVERABLE ADDRESSES TO NATIONAL GEOGRAPHIC, PO BOX 4412 STN. A, TORONTO, ONTARIO M5W 3W2. UNITED KINGDOM NEWSSTAND PRICE £4.50. REPR. EN FRANCE: EMD FRANCE SA, BP 1029, 59011 LILLE CEDEX; TEL. 320.300.302; CPPAP NO. 0710U89037; DIRECTEUR PUBLICATION: TASSINARI DOMENICO DIR. RESP. ITALIA; RAPPR. IMD SRL, VIA G. DA VELATE 11-20162 MILANO; AUT. TRIB. MI N. 258 26/5/84; SPED. ABB. POST. 45% ART.2 COMMA 20/B LEGGE 23/12/96 N.662 MILANO STAMPATA QUAD/GRAPHICS, MARTINSBURG, WV 25401. MEMBERS: IF THE POSTAL SERVICE ALERTS US THAT YOUR MAGAZINE IS UNDELIVERABLE, WE HAVE NO FURTHER OBLIGATION UNLESS WE RECEIVE A CORRECTED ADDRESS WITHIN TWO YEARS.

1	2	3	4	■	5	6	7	8	■	9	10	11	12	13
14				■	15				■	16				
17				18					■	19				
■	■	■	■	20					■	21				
22	23	24	25					■	26					
27					■	■	■	28			■	29		
30					31	32	33				34	■	■	■
35				■	36					■	37	38	39	40
■	■	■	41	42						43				
44	45	46	■	47			■	■	■	48				
49			50			■	51	52	53					
54					■	55					■	■	■	■
56					■	57					58	59	60	61
62					■	63				■	64			
65					■	66				■	67			

Bound for Glory

Puzzle by Cathy Allis

Ancient Egyptians' ties to animals (a scene on a sarcophagus is at left) extended even to the afterlife. Creatures were wrapped in linen or papyrus to serve as a human mummy's best friends. Read the animal mummies story on page 30. Then unravel the tinted clues.

ACROSS

1 Medium of 1932's *The Mummy*
5 Go the distance
9 Kvetches
14 Figment
15 George S. Kaufman collaborator Ferber
16 *Silas Marner* author George
17 With 22 Across, animal mummy parts?
19 Nick of *48 Hrs.*
20 Figure skating category
21 Eighth Greek letter
22 See 17 Across
26 Examined a mummy, in a way
27 Book before Joel
28 *Jungle Book* python
29 Ones tapping IRAs
30 It transports natron to bunny mummifier Ikram
35 Like the wind in a Shelley ode
36 Map detail
37 British mil. awards
41 Feature of some well-preserved cat mummies found in an 1888 dig?
44 "Help wanted!"
47 Anti's cry
48 A counting rhyme's start
49 Clanlike
51 "Here Comes Peter Cottontail," for his mummy experimenters?
54 Craft carrying crude
55 Don, the longtime Dolphins coach
56 Kingdom
57 One performing a mummification step on a cottontail's kin?
62 Newbery-winning author Madeleine L'__
63 Wing-shaped
64 River that was a battle site in 38 Down
65 Jouster's mount
66 Prepare frankincense for sealing mummies, e.g.
67 Give off

DOWN

1 Looking buff
2 Gilbert and Sullivan princess
3 Part of a Waikiki welcome
4 Function or practice prefix
5 King Arthur adversary Morgan __
6 Trickling with moisture
7 Quickly downed shot
8 Skye caps
9 Component of CPU
10 Part of a Waikiki welcome
11 Poet James Whitcomb and kin
12 Craftsperson at a wheel
13 Positions usually held by others
18 Jack whose wife ate fat
22 Soften before serving
23 Running wear?
24 Sp. fem. "those"
25 Gaels and Bretons
26 Hobby knife "handle"
28 Ukraine capital whence a chicken dish name
31 Rapidly spreading, as marketing
32 A deadly sin
33 Confucian philosopher Chu __
34 Outer limits
38 __-Japanese War
39 *Havana* actress Lena
40 Retired plush buddy of Rex and Bronty
42 Having no piece?
43 Give new cushioning
44 Big boxes, perhaps
45 Show the ropes
46 Fodder that's stored
50 Southern ball standout
51 Baleen is one type
52 Countrified
53 It may be amber or red
55 Mud wrapped as a mummy, for instance
58 Ingredient in a wet or dry toast?
59 Thanksgiving tuber
60 Inventor Whitney
61 Dirt road indentation

Answers in Inside Geographic

PHOTO: RICHARD BARNES